Ame

Time for High Speed Steel Wheel

And

Maglev Trains

No Winglock No Weather Delays
No Waiting No Cancellations
No Secutity Checks

By

Andrew D. Anderson

ISBN: 1-4033-7392-2 (e-book)
ISBN: 1-4033-7393-0 (Paperback)
ISBN: 1-4033-7394-9 (Hardcover)

This book is printed on acid free paper.

1stBooks - rev. 03/08/04

Acknowledgments

I am most grateful to my dear wife Bessie and her help, support, cooperation, and patience, my son Nathan and wife Joyce that planted the seed and provided encouragement and research material, my grandchildren, Danielle and Eric in Merrimack, New Hampshire, my daughter Angela and granddaughter Dominique in California, Terry and Teresa Smith and grandchildren, and Daryll in Columbus, Ohio. I also want to thank Computer Rescue for the technical assistance, advice, and voluntary service.

Preface

There are three transportation systems we use for travel, vehicle, airplane, and train. The vehicle has changed our life styles, increased suburban development, decreased the number of isolated small-towns, and increased traffic congestion causing more pollution. Everything is geared toward getting more vehicles on our crowded roadways. The high schools have drivers' training classes where the individual is soon awarded driver's license giving the driver the ability to escape parental supervision and extend the horizons while distance barriers fade.

The privacy and flexibility of our personal vehicles must be balanced against the discomfort of its seats, the traffic and congestion on the roaways, the probability of an accident, people getting killed in large numbers on our highways, and others having disabilities the rest of their lives. Yet the vehicle gives the feeling of control over our destiny even when we are crawling along on a congested part of a wide interstate highway. We do not even think about the accumulative delayed time in traffic going nowhere fast, the wasted gasoline used sitting in traffic, and the increased smog levels vehicles produce that could be overcome by riding a Commuter Rail train.

Air travel has produced more level of service time for the traveler. Included are winglock, gridlock, airport delays, cancellation, weather uncertainties, long security check lines, and long walks to the gate where the travelers have no control. The travelers are not just interested in going from one airport to another airport, but interested in going from an origin to a destination and the time it takes to get there.

Air travel also puts us in even less comfortale seats with little leg room. We went from being served full course dinners to a bag of pretzel or peanuts, and the seats were moved closer behind each other permitting less leg room. Their analyst figured how the airlines could make more money by reducing the passengers comforts since they had high riderships, they continued to grow, and competition was not a consideration.

Both modes of transportation have limitations and are vulnerable to fluctuations in our oil energy supply that is coverted into pollution. The Airlines and vehicles have a controlling affect on our lives and we agree to it by continuing to use them.

This book emphasize the relevance of the three transportation systems to satisfy the needs of the travelers economically, travel time, and more comforts without each overlapping systems generating confusion when making choices.

Japan had a steel-wheel Bullet Train running since the 1950s and has carried many passengers without any fatalities. Now in 2002 America has a new train called the Acela Amtrak with a top speed of 150 mph operating on the East Coast.

It has a new way of traveling that is efficient and safe with a good environment and is a steel-wheel aerodynamic shaped train designed for speed and comforts. It has new wheel-sets, a suspension systems that tilt the cars on curves reducing the centrifugal force for passenger comforts, computerized signaling, and the cars are lighter in weight. The rails are continuous with no joints for smooth quiet movement. When the passengers boards the train they see the interior of a pretty coach with warm comfortable colors, pretty carpets on the floors, and a quietness that does not identify a train. Reservations can be made over the telephone before arriving and the conductor accepts credit cards. The seats are side-by-side with a distance of 42 inches between them and large sized padded armrest, headrest, trays, and the seats have dampers that eliminate vibrations caused by any movements.

There are plugs for portable computers and a flip on switch that turns on your individual television. Passengers can sit at any of 32 convenient tables throughout the train in swivel seats. When walking in the moving train there is no side-to-side movement and it has automatic opening doors between cars. The dinning room is designed like a first class cafe and you have two choices of wine with dinner. Complete meals can be purchased for $6.95 and $7.95.

Passengers are given points for their gift certificates that are good for renting cars, many exclusive hotels, and retailers. The passengers can receive free rides after a certain number of trips on the train and it is an enjoyable experience to look out the big windows while enjoying the comforts of the ride.

More steel-wheel trains will be built to be used in California, Texas, Nevada and Illinois just to name a few. Illinois is planning for an inter-city system. Chicago, being the hub, is to have a line linking Chicago with Detroit and St. Louis. A second link from Chicago linking Milwaukee, Minneapolis, and a third line linking Chicago's O'Hare airport. Texas is planning a rail system linking Dallas, Fort Worth, Austin, Houston, and San Antonio that will run directly into the Dallas-Fort Worth Airport stopping at American Airline and Delta Airline gates so baggage and passengers can be easily unloaded and loaded between planes and trains.

A new train will be manufactured called Magnetic Levitation. It has a resemblance to the appearance of conventional trains, but it does not ride on rails. The whole train is lifted and held upward by currents passing over iron cores that reacts with other magnets in the guideway. The principal is like magnets that attrack or repel. It has speeds up to 300 mph and will travel a distance of 500 miles. Japan, German, and Switzerland have maglev trains operating with no fatalities in over a million miles.

It is powered by electricity, and will reduce the demand for less acceptable types of energy consumption like gasoline in vehicles, and kerosene in jet airplanes. The total petroleum savings over 16 corridors for the year of 2020 are estimated to be 21 million barrels for the maglev. It has good acceleration/breaking that permits speeds over four times the highway speed limit of 65 mph posted speeds, one rail mile is equilvant to ten lanes of highway, and one train carries 300 passengers which is equilvant to 300 vehicles. Time between schedules can be changed to move more passengers in a given time.

It has no congestion and weather conditions that air or highway does giving high reliability. There is a large index of comfort compared to air travel, with no air turbulence ensuring a cosistantly smooth and quiet ride.

Short-distance travel of 500 miles represents more than 25 percent of the trips handled to and from O'Hare in Chicago and ten busy airports. The steel-wheel and the maglev trains would provide needed help reducing congestion, confusion, and travel time.

High speed ground travel is based on the number of current air trips less than 600 mile distance because trips diverted from air travel have shown to be the largest source of revenue. Trip time includes estimates for terminal egress and acess time at both ends of the trip as well as time spent in terminals for train or airplane. On trips up to 500 mile distance when totaled, the air mode of travel advantage over maglev is generally eliminated or reduced.

Fares will compete with air fares and are lowered where the maglev travel time is larger and maglev's trip time compared to auto modes is shorter when long distances are considered.

America is expected to build three types of maglev systems: metropolitan feeders, inter-city corridors vs inner-city, and multi-state networks. The feeder systems would connect outlying metropolitan areas with its core starting 125 miles out with stations approximately 15 miles apart. The big cities would use maglev feeders along the inter-states. A future National Maglev Network would be similar to the interstate highway systems going through 42 states with a maximum speed of 300 mph.

I have written this book not only to provide information for busy people, but to cover a crosssections of events that we have now and some ways we contribute to worldwide warming. We may not be aware of some things that are taking place overseas and in America, but we must realize this is all one planet. What happens in one part affects all of our lives. I have provided relevant events based on airplanes and our other fuel burning vehicles as contributors to our health in an effort to show the need for more use of trains for our transportation. We cannot turn back time, but we can all participate in ways in the present and in the future that will slow some of the events that are changing our lives.

The text is divided into chapters and parts with page numbers to help locate specific information. Each gives direct clues to what is in the chapter to help the reader and the prospective buyer that scans the Contents to reinforce what it covers.

Contents

Chapter 3: The Airlines We Fly

Chapter 4: America is Growing

Chapter 5: Worldwide Warming

Chapter 6: Amtrak-The Old and The New

Illustrations

List of Tables

Chapter 1: Slaves to Vehicles We Drive

Introduction

The purpose of this book is to introduce the reader to the three transportation systems we use to move about, vehicles, airplanes, new steel-wheel trains, and magnetic levitation trains that travel 300 mph to be in use soon in the United States. The focus is on basic principles of our transportation modes and uses the three modes to compare the reliability, cost, delays, trip time, distance traveled, comforts, and safety.

Vehicle cost analyses are based on Annual Roadway Congestion Index & Cost values, Annual Travel Delays Per Eligible Driver-Capita, Annual Wasted Fuel Per Eligible Driver-Capita, and the death and disabling caused by the light weight light constructed vehicles we drive. Airports and trains are introduced as one network where a distance traveler gets off of an airplane onto a train with links to the inner-city, and commuter-rails from inter-city to suburban areas.

Vehicles Causing Transportation Problems

The transportation problems we have today is derived by the fossil fuel burning vehicles and airplanes the government pays for, and the number of obsolete passenger trains that run on old railroad tracks we subsidized. We emphasize the new steel-wheel and 300 mph magnetic levitation trains that has years of safe records of over a million miles of dependent service in France, Germany, Italy, and Japan with no fatalities. Japan had its first Bullet Trains running in the 1950s.

The information focus on developing, measures and a range of transportation improvement as a broadband set of measures that analyze mobility from a multimodal perspective system level. The craze for more and more miles of highway is equated by the lust for more and more cars, but in this age, it takes longer to get to work than it did when the trolleys ruled the road.

Any change in the rules designed to reduce the numbers of vehicles being driven must guarantee relief now based on facts. It must provide for a fast and comfortable alternative to the auto as a means of commuting to work during peak periods. And it must promise one more important thing, a tangible regard for giving up something as enjoyable and convenient as driving one's own car to work. The effects of our daily mobility and congestions are spread all over America and affects the movement of people and goods.

The approach is relevant to all transportation modes and geographic locations on a premise that our three modes of transportation has to be based on fundamental principles integraded with each of the three transportation system that moves people. It is an integral part of our everyday lives and has impacts on all people.

State and local agencies have looked at various effects listed below for an improvement of vehicle congestions, but that time has passed.

1. Increase vanpools and bus lane use
2. Reduce the number of vehicles where possible.
3. Vary the work times.
4. Increased road space or lanes on expressways.
5. Transit improvements
6. Coordinating traffic signals to speed traffic

The Prices We Pay

Congestion cost US travelers 4.6 billion hours of delay, 6.7 billion gallons of wasted fuel consumed, and $74 billion of time and fuel cost in 1996. The percent of congested peak period travel on the freeways at least tripled between 1982 and 1996 in 20 urban areas. The percent of congested peak period freeway travel at least double in 23 other urban areas between 1982 and 1996. In total 53 urban areas showed increases of at least 50 percent in congested peak period freeway travel between 1982-1996 and the percentages will continue to grow.

Congestion is anything that slows the regular flow of traffic whether it is on the freeway, or principal arterial streets.

We went from a slow ride in an automobile with no door on the drivers side and talked loud because of the noisy engine with no radio driving on narrow rough roads. Now we have wide four and six lane expressways and we ride in comforts, but we cannot enjoy or relax because of the heavy traffic and lost time going from one place to the other while breathing polluted air. Even in some places the green trees along roads show signs of being affected by the pollution.

For years our automobiles gave us a feeling of freedom, and even the automobile-tanks sold (over size automobiles in the 50s) allowed us to ignore limitations. As drivers, we were our own masters. We moved about more easily than any other people in history worldwide. But this has become a problem with less and less freedom causing gridlock's during peak and off peak hours. In the fifties, our vehicles rested between the hours of the commute at midday, and roads were empty. At night the vehicle rested in the postwar boom as we ate our dinners and read the newspapers.

We have added time behind the wheel for space in the suburbs as work-bound Americans travel back and forth from ever-more sprawling homes where farmers fields grew crops for our tables. Our vehicles once made it better to get to and increasing number of jobs and move to the urban areas to live in big oversized houses, and we thought we needed two or three vehicles and one was usually a 4 x 4. We did this not fully by choice, or any desire for wanted freedom of the road.

In subsidizing the vehicles and highways, we have short changed every other mode of transportation, altered settlement patterns, and used accepted obeisance in the vehicles. With the United States being behind in moving people in and out of cities, we have been so brainwashed that we think we have no other alternatives with the love of our vehicles.

We drive with one person in the vehicle increasing the numbers on the road, and in the process pollute our environments and speed up global warming. We are vehicle-bound by vehicle dependency because we have not been provided another acceptable means of mobility. Based on today's life styles, the notion that the road offers romantic vision of freedom is a fantasy which overlooks the realities and try to satisfy our imagination driven by our wants.

The government pays "seven" times as much to support the operation of the private vehicles as to support public transportation. That does not sound like much, but when you use a figure of $7 billion for highways, the transit system gets $1 billion. Our surroundings are paved cities for parking lots infiltrating our countryside's with large concrete-wrapped malls, new houses, and new schools that are high in demand and increasing.

In 1990, 429 million passengers traveled 342 billion passenger miles on commercial airlines. Two trillion passenger miles were traveled by truck, bus, car, and 6.1 billion passengers miles on the old Amtrak. Those riders traveled on overcrowded highways and waited in congested airports for delayed or cancelled flights.

Smog Levels and Our Health

The poisons discharges in the air from tailpipes and from water run off from farmers fertilized fields into our waterways are well known, but it is only a small part of the damage. Road kill occurs on many level. Lives lost because of vehicle fatalities, chronic assaults on health, lost of habitat, and accelerating our global warming that heats up our planet. Add land lost for hardtopping 30 to 40 percent of our cities. We are working with existing systems by widening roads that carries a price tag of $6.6 billion and having more fatalities in lightweight unsafe vehicles built to give better gas mileage and providing less safety.

In 1991 there were 74 million people in the US residing in counties that were not in compliance with national ambient air quality standards. Ozone and carbon monoxide levels have the highest degrees of non-attainment, while sulfur dioxide has the lowest.

Motor vehicles cause $40 to $50 billion in annual health-care expenditures and many are unnecessary or premature deaths said Thomas Gaudier president of the American Lung Association. The Clean Air Act will not solve the problems because the rules have been watered down at the insistence of lobbyist. Now more than 200 US cities exceed the maximum permissible ozone levels at some point each year. Many cities are always above the permitted amounts and it will only get worst. What good does the Clean Act do? It may sound good, but its not trying to get people on trains that causes very little pollution.

Hydrocarbon emissions in exhaust from internal combustion engines is bad for our bodies. Gasoline is a mixture of liquid hydrocarbons that have a variety of boiling points. Only the most volatile components of gasoline vaporize and burn when a cold engine first turns over. Up to 80 percent of the unburned hydrocarbons emitted during a typical 30-minute drive is generated during the first 2 minutes of engine warm-up.

Cutting emission will help automakers meet the agency's tougher tailpipe standards scheduled to be phased in beginning in 2004.

Economic growth and limited environmental restrictions have turned urban areas in Eastern Texas into air pollution hot spots. Texas had the smoggiest days in September of 1999 than all the United States for ozone, a key ingredient at summer time temperatures that causes lung tissues to stiffen based on preliminary data.

Ground-level ozone is the most prevalent air pollutant in Texas and the nation. Ozone is formed by chemical reactions of volatile organic compounds and nitrogen oxides, both of which are emitted by vehicles and construction equipment. Ozone concentration contributes to smog formation and negatively affects health, especially for children and high-risk individuals or people who spend long hours outdoors. Prolonged exposure to high concentration of ozone also damages products made from "rubber, nylon, plastic, and places food crops at risk."

Fort Worth, Texas has the highest parts of ozone as businesses and employees have been moving to Texas causing many urban homes to be built. The more urban dwellers you have commuting the more ozone will be generated. Texas is an ideal place for high readings of ozone and it had a series of 100 degree temperatures in a low humidity state.

Air quality legislation passed in 1990 restricted federal transportation funds to any area failing to meet air quality standards and conform to certain requirements associated with achieving those standards. Texas and many other states are faced with air quality conditions that will be hazardous to the long term health of residents says Brian Bother.

Areas not meeting the standards in 1990 were given schedules for improving their air quality. The schedules were based on the severity of each area's air quality deficiencies. Each deficient area has a deadline for achieving attainment with the most severely deficient areas to reach standards no later than 2010, The Environmental Agency initially designated over 100 areas as nonattainment. The soot and gases emitted by heavy-duty diesel trucks and buses also damage air quality and are considered in the nonattainment.

The United States has to seek ways to reduce the pollution, but as the United States population keeps growing and more vehicles are purchase, we cannot stop it. The best we can hope to do is slow it. As more pollution is reduced, more vehicles will be in operation and the smog will continue, but more lives will be saved.

See table 1.1 for the ozone level in some cities in ascending order. Fort Worth, TX is the worst.

Table 1.1

Ozone Levels

Required One Hour Ozone Limit is 124 Parts Per Billion

153 Arlington, TX	163 Arlington, TX	176 Galveston, TX
154 Congress, GA	167 Middletown, CT	178 Dambury, CT
157 Atlanta, GA	170 Crestline, CA	185 Houston, TX
158 Standford, CT	171 White Plains, NY	188 Westport, CT
162 Danvers, TX	172 Texas City, TX	209 Fort Worth, TX

Source: Office of General Councel, US Department of Transporation

The Dollars We Lose

The expensive vehicles we buy cost an average price of about $24,000 said Jan Holtxz Hay. There is a yearly cost of about $4,000 to pay for policing and parking facilities, environmental damage and uncompensated accidents plus approximated $6,000 a year for maintenance, insurance, and out of the pocket cost. Some other expensive we have are over $72 billion in local, state, and federal money for the highways each year.

The cost of building the Century Freeway in Los Angeles cost $2.2 billion years ago and would cost much more now. In 1989 Seattle, Washington opened only seven miles of an interstate highway at a cost of $1.46 billion, but the addition helped only for a short time.

Stop and Go Traffic During Peak Periods

Since we are on this earth only for a few years, why waste a large part of that time sitting in oversize, over powered, and over designed expensive vehicles that have plastic where the two major impact areas are? One person per vehicle usually travel alone going to work and breathing toxins while the blood pressure rise. It has been estimated that as a nation we spend 8 billion hours a year sitting in traffic. The total lost for America is equated to be "$51 billion" a year on wasted fuel burned going nowhere sitting in congested traffic.

Americans like comfort and independence in this high technology period in our vehicles, but do not see the capacity of expansion on environmental destructive matters that our modes of travel give. All of the new cars and trucks sold every year force more freeways to be built and cause more man-hours to be lost on the freeways trying to get somewhere.

The American Automobile Association identified the 10 worst bottlenecks ranked by number of cars driving through them daily in 1995.

1. Los Angeles: Interstate 5 at the intersection of I-10, state Routes 60, and 101 had 566,000 vehicles per day.
2. Houston: More than 330,000 cars travel the cross of US 59 and the 610 loop each day causing five to six hours of congestion.
3. Dallas: Over 200,000 drivers go through I-35 and I-30, which is known as the "mix master."
4. Boston: I-93 at Route 128 and Route 3 at 128. I-93 was built in the 1950s for 90,000 vehicles a day, but now has 190,000 vehicles. The stop-and-go traffic lasts four to six hours.
5. New York: A typical day on the 3.8 mile stretch of the Gowns Expressway between the Brooklyn Battery Tunnel and the Belt Parkway has six hours of delays.
6. New Orleans: Approximately 174,000 vehicles travel through I-10 and I-610 where lanes drop from three to two and visibility is restricted.
7. Washington DC: Three mile backups are common on the Capital Beltway which is the results of eight lanes becoming six where the Woodwork Wilson Bridge crosses the Potomac.
8. Milwaukee: Patches of I-94 designed to handle 80,000 vehicles per day are jammed with 160,000 vehicles per day.

9. Minneapolis: Every day 100,000 vehicles go North into downtown on three lanes of I-35W at Minneehaha Creek.

A detail look at Los Angeles's dilemma for 566,000 vehicles daily. In a 24 hour period that's 23,583 vehicles every hour, 393 every minute, and 6-1/2 cars per second. This is possible because of the lanes of traffic that cross each other with traffic that does not stop. If you ask owners why they have a vehicle, the usually answers are to commute to work, travel in during vacations, carry the children to their activities, and drive to the store to buy goods. Yet some of the same people sit at a computer terminal trying to determine a cost effective way for a million dollar corporation to make a bigger profit. They do not figure the cost for commuting twenty miles to work with only one person in an oversize vehicle or how efficient it is to drive a 2,500 pound vehicle through traffic lights to a store two miles away. The complete gasoline, oil, wear, including tires and battery, and the stress on the driver to get a carton of milk on a spur of the moment, is not considered.

Motor Vehicle Deaths, Disabilities, and Surgery

We usually drive 10,000 to 12,000 miles a year, double the distance two decades ago, in congestion effecting our lives and our landscapes. Our engineers and planners have highway ramps that mark our surroundings, paved cities for parking lots, and infiltrating suburbs and countryside's with concrete malls. We hardtop 30 to 40 percent of our cities and asphalt thousands of acres of productive farm land each year. We have to un-do our auto dependency.

A large portion of our costs are based on the vehicles we drive causing accidents. National Spinal Cord Injury Statistical Center estimated in "1988," first year medical cost for a high quadriplegic at $417,000 plus $74,000 for each year thereafter. When and if the private insurance company stops paying the cost, it will usually be paid by Medicare.

Casualties involved in road crashes often sustain multiple injuries, yet very little is known about the cost of injuries. Surgery for thoracotomies, surgical incision of the chest wall, average cost was $26,000 and for laparotomies, opening of the abdomen by an incision where a variety of surgical procedures maybe used subsequent to the openings with an average cost of $41,000 plus $74,707 more each year thereafter, For a twenty year old quadriplegic with a life span of forty years, the life time medical cost would be $3.77 million for that one person.

Some average cost of road crash casualties with single injuries by body region for 2001.

1. Head	$68,000	2. Spine	$42,000	3. Upper Leg	$33,000
4. Lower Leg	$31,000	5. Face	$16,000	6. Neck	$11,000

Death tolls have increased every year since 1899 when Mr. H. H. Bliss, a New Yorker, got off a trolley and was killed by a horse drawn carriage. In the United States, vehicles caused its first million dead by 1952, its second million by 1975 and the third million by 1994 wrote Andrew Kimberell. Along the way, some 90 million Americans sustained disabling injuries in auto accidents. In all, more than 2.5 million Americans who have died violent deaths on our highways represent more than four times the Americans killed in World War 1, World War II, Korea, and Vietnam wars combined said Andrew Kimberell. For most of the Americans, it does not really matter unless it is a friend or relative.

Table 1.2 shows the vehicle accidents and deaths for the years showned.

Table 1.2

Motor Vehicle Accidents and Deaths 1994-1997
(14.3 represents 14,300,000) (180 represents 180,000)

Item	Unit	1994	1995	1996	1997
Motor vehicle accidents (1)					
Cars	Million	14.3	12.3	13.3	16.1
Trucks	Million	4.4	4.5	4.8	7.7
Motorcycles	1,000	180	152	135	138
Most vehicle deaths (2)	1,000	46.8	43.4	43.3	43.2
Noncollision Accidents	1,000	4.9	4.4	4.5	4.2
Collision Accidents					
With other motor vehicles	1,000	19.9	19.1	19.5	21.3
With fixed objects	1,000	13.1	12.1	12.3	10.8
With pedestrains	1,000	7.3	6.4	5.8	5.7
Death within 30 days	1,000	44.6	41.8	41.9	41.9
Vehicle-occupants	1,000	33.9	33.1	33.4	33.6
Pedestrian	1,000	7.5	5.6	5.4	5.2
Motorcyclists (3)	1,000	3.2	3.1	3.1	3.1
Total deaths within 1 year and 30 days after accident	1,000	91.4	85.2	85.2	85.1

Source: National Safety Council, Itasca, IL

(1) Covers only accidents on road.
(2) Deaths that occur within 1 year of accident includes collision categories not shown.
(3) Includes motor scooters, motorized bicycles, and mopeds.

The Insurance Institute for Highway Safety said, motor-vehicle accidents in the United States cause one motor-vehicle death every "11" minutes and an injury every 18 seconds. The accident rates will continue through the year 2020 with projected travel volumes twice today's and is estimated that about 100 million people will die each year on our nation's highways.

Public Relations said, the large amount of fatalities on our highways every year is the price of progress and convenience. The Coalition for Consumer Health and Safety says, motor-vehicle crashes are the leading killer of Americans under the age 35 and the leading cause of head injuries, epilepsy, quadipleg, paraplegia, facial injuries, as well as a significant cause of blindness. Each year 1.6 million people suffer disabling injures resulting from such accidents. When the vehicular wreckage is towed away, the human wreckage is left behind.

The durability, weight, and crashworthiness of the vehicles we drive are dependent upon the material they are made of. The United States said the majority of the vehicles would get a certain mpg, but did not put many limitations on how this should be obtained. Naturally the first thing considered was the weight of the vehicles. Lighter weight vehicles requires less energy to move and stop, but there is a safety trade-off and more people are killed at the cost of getting more mpg. More cost is added by removing crashed vehicles and vehicle break downs. There is no comparison when viewing pictures of crashes on the highways today and those taken in the 1950s.

Based on data from the 1992 National Transportation Statistics, the rate of fatalities involving passenger cars and taxis has risen slowly reaching 1.11% per 10 passenger miles traveled in 1990. For accidents involving inter-city passenger trains, the average fatality rate including grade crossing accidents since 1985 is about 0.54 per 10 passenger miles traveled. For scheduled commercial flights, the fatality rate average over periods 1985 to 1990 was about 0.08 per 10 passenger miles traveled.

Congestion Cost per Driver-Capita

Roadway Congestion Index (RCI) is a way of measuring a vehicle travel density on major roadways used in urban areas for commuting.

An RCI of 1.0 is a desirable congestion level and anything over that is undesirable on principal arterial streets and freeways during peak periods. In some instances when the RCI is less than 1.0, there may be still some areas where congestion is a temporary problem.

The cost of congestion is estimated by applying hourly values to the amount of travel time delay and per-gallon estimates of the amount of fuel wasted in congested travel. Costs associated with congestion cannot proceed without public support for funding the projects or programs whose repairs eliminate the congestion. Any life style changes, alternative land use, or new transportation strategies has to be approved.

Congestion is growing faster than the population. It's outpaced the growth in registered drivers and vehicles on the road. It is growing faster as the increasing number of miles Americans drive each year and the number of drivers should dictate how bad our traffic jams are, but congestion has been a much bigger monster than it was thought to be. The population has grown 22 percent in the nation's biggest urban areas over the past 15 years and congestion has grown 235 percent. California has 25 percent major bottlenecks followed by Texas with 18 percent, and Ohio with 14 percent. They have the mixing bowl in Northern Virginia, the big I in Albuquerque, New Mexico, and the big dig in Boston.

The number of vehicles registered in this country has surged from a million in 1970 to 208 million in 1997. The number of miles driven has increased 127 percent over 27 years from 1.1 million to 2.5 million miles annually. Congestion delays nationwide have surged 150 percent since 1970 engineer Omstead said.

Congestion levels are higher in the larger urban areas, and decline as population decreases. Only five urban areas, Tacoma, Tampa, New Orleans, Houston, and Phoenix showed short-term decreases in congestion level in the period between 1992 and 1997. Two other urban areas had a decrease in their congestion levels for the period between 1982 and 1996. The major reason for the decline in Houston and Phoenix congestion levels were large construction efforts over the past decade, but could not continue to remain the same because of the increased number of houses being built and people moving into the urban areas increasing the number of vehicles used.

If new roadways and facilities cause the RCI to decrease, it is for a short period because new roadways and facilities cannot be built fast enough to accommodate that year's growth. New construction is usually widening existing roads for space, adding new roads, and using vehicle and bus/pools. When more lanes are added to freeways, there is a point where the number of lanes will decrease causing back up traffic on the new lanes added. The only way adding new lanes for a distance will temporarily help is having new lanes continually added before they converge to less lanes and it has to be in less populated areas. It does not take long for roadways to again fill with traffic and the congestion level begins to increase causing expensive no win solutions.

Planners have to look at the costs associated with congestion in the amount of roadway that will be needed every year to maintain a constant level of congestion if possible. This indicates that in fast growing areas it is impossible to afford the road construction budget cost. The percentage of travel in the worst congested conditions more than doubled from about 15 percent in 1982 to about 35 percent in 1996.

The effects of congestion is integrated with movement of people, merchandise, productivity, and time. Each with a busy life have become conditioned to the time each travelers spends on the roads, the extra cost of wasted fuel, the cost of delays, and the stress put in our lives.

Congestion index and cost values depend on driving conditions and inefficient operation that waste fuel. Traffic violations that risk accidents, traffic citations, road repair, accidents, and abrupt lane changing contribute to wasted fuel.

See table 1.3 for the annual congestion levels per driver, the annual congestion cost for cities listed for the same years, and the annual average speeds for freeways and principal arterial streets. In 1996, the annual congestion cost per driver in Los Angeles was $1,205 and the annual city congestion cost in Los Angeles was $10.705 billion just for the cost of congestion. The value of 1.52 is fifty two percent higher than recommended.

Table 1.3

Annual Congestion Index and Cost Values 1994 to 1996-Speeds 1996
($10.705 represents $10,750,000,000)

Urban Areas	Roadway Indexes 1994	Roadway Indexes 1996	Annual Cost per Driver 1994	Annual Cost per Driver 1996	Annual Cost per City 1994	Annual Cost per City 1996	Speeds mph FW 1996	Speeds mph AS 1996
Los Angeles, CA	1.52	1.57	$1,035	$1,205	$9,185	$10,705	35	28
Washington DC, MD, VA	1.43	1.43	1,030	1,290	2,930	3,655	39	26
Chicago II-NW-IN	1.28	1.34	545	670	3,225	4,005	40	27
Miami-Healeah, FL	1.32	1.34	789	905	1,195	1,460	13	13
San Francisco-Oakland, CA	1.33	1.33	975	1,055	3,000	3,250	38	28
Seattle-Everett WA	1.24	1.27	955	1,155	1,495	1,780	37	29
Atlanta, GA	1.18	1.24	850	1,095	1,595	2,110	42	27
Detroit, MI	1.24	1.24	860	1,095	2,655	3,165	6	6
San Bernardino, CA	1.21	1.22	890	1,030	855	990	39	29

Source: Texas Transportation Institute, Texas A&M University
FW represents freeway
AS represents asterrial streets

Information from Texas Transportation Institute Texas A&M University is used as a reference. The annual traffic congestion study was an effort to monitor roadway congestion in major urban areas in the United States. The effects of congestion is widespread and effects the movement of people and goods. There is an increased travel time, increased fuel consumption in stop and go traffic, and lost productivity of people and freight moving vehicles. Congestion also affects the efficiency of just in-time manufacturing processes.

Crashes or vehicle breakdowns increase travel time and can mean components do not arrive in time to be installed on schedule, or businesses must keep larger inventories to accommodate unreliable delivery schedules. The report evaluated travel conditions, operations on freeways, and principal arterial street networks from 1986 to 1996.

Just In Time Deliveries

The terrorist attack in September 2001, opened another field of vision for the American people. American manufacturers copied from the Japanese car companies in the 1980s on how to temporarily save millions of dollars. Spending millions of dollars on merchandise kept for a period of time in inventory could be used elsewhere. Carrying a small inventory to keep their factories operating for a limited time reduced the size of inventories freeing funds for other uses. Robert Sustain, assistant professor at Harvard Business School said, it was like keeping money in your closet.

Before the terrorist attack, the manufacturers did not look at the probability of a slow down in getting parts. Many of the supplies and parts used were made and delivered from countries like Canada and Taiwan. Drivers in the fifty mile backups of tractor-trailers passing the Canadian checkpoint waited up to twelve hours to pass. The Ford Motor Company shut down five of its United States plants because they could not get enough engines and other parts from the suppliers in Canada because of the delays. It took one half of a day to clear United States customs. This meant they had been using the just-in-time system.

Dell Computer Corporation is the world's leading maker of desktop computers and most of the parts are shipped from manufacturers in Asia. They had been so confidence they maintained five days of inventory. Manufacturers using parts made in American had no problems and will continue the just-in-time deliveries that helped power the economic boom. The other companies getting parts from overseas to save a few dollars will have to consider, just-in-case, for a complete system.

Annual Delays Going Nowhere Fast

Since more people are moving to urban areas as big new houses are continually built, a broader range of solutions is needed to make progress in mobility now and in the future. Using vehicles only compounds the problems and more congestion occurs, more money is spent, and there will be more accidents and death while the congestion continues to exists and grow.

The Federal Highway Administration estimates that vehicle delays during peak travel periods due to congestion, will increase 400 percent in urban areas from 1985 too 2005. A study made by the Texas Transportation Institute of Texas A&M University System in a 1998 report said, the average increase for all 70 urban areas studied in delay per driver was 208 percent between 1982 and 1996.

US travelers had 4.6 billion hours of delays and 6.7 billion gallons of wasted fuel consumed in 1996. Addressing these problem will not require one transportation system, but a range of specific systems and strategies.

The annual hours of delay experienced by urban areas in 1996 varied from a low of about 955,000 hours in Boulder, Colorado to 684 million hours in Los Angles, CA which is a much bigger area. However, the average annual delay for the 70 urban areas studied was about 65 million hours. The drivers spent at least one-half of a work week (20 Hours) per year to over two work weeks annually in delays which is more than a two week vacation.

A typical commuter will spend a total of over five years of life just stuck in traffic said Douglas I. Foy, executive director of the Conservation Law Foundation of New England. That's five years that could be used for a number of things if just for enjoying life.

The drain of the economy in delays, productivity, and other costs, such as fuel consumption and accidents, will reach $40 billion in the year 2005 according to the American Association of State Highway and Transportation Officials. The federal government is spending more on highways, and the 42,798 mile intestates network is almost complete. The price tag should reach $122 billion. Americas interstate program is the largest public works project in the history of the world, but mobility does not increase despite the large expenditures. There are always cost over-runs and some are increased by 800 percent.

Traveling delay is most impacted in roadway congestion and conditions of roadways that causes an increase in wasted fuel and deducts from the time we spend here on earth. The total is the addition of the recurring and incident items.

Recurring delay is the increase in travel time during peak periods of travel that is caused by slower speeds because of congestions on principal arterial streets and freeways as heavy traffic, tolls, or reduced speed limits.

Incident delays are also an increase in travel time during peak periods. These incidents are breakdowns, vehicle accidents, or stalled vehicles that decreases roadway capacity temporarily. The full figures of actual recurring and incident times are used to emphasize the size of the numbrs.

The annual person-hours of delay in Washington, DC is 82 hours per year. That is two hours over a two week vacation and the total delays are 2.3 million hours lost for the District. An inner-city train could “eliminate” that number of hours and could be used for productive time even if some time is spent laying on the beech in the summer.

The delay per driver and per capita estimates show the penalties in wasted time all motorists and citizens pay because of these congested roadways, but really do not consider the impact it has on our life and the accumulative effect in time. A transportation train network could elimate most of the lost time. See table 1.4 for the annual hours of delay per driver and the annual delays per capita based on the number of eligible drivers.

Table 1.4

Annual Delay Hours per Driver and Total Annual Delay Hours per City Due To Congestion in 1996

Urban Area	Annual Delay per Driver	Annual Delay per City Recurring	Incident	Total
Los Angeles, CA	76	315,265,000	369,145,000	684,410,000
New York, NY, NE, NJ	44	211,280,000	400,140,000	611,420,000
Chicago, IL, NW, IN	42	116,210,000	134,630,000	250,840,000
Washington, DC, MD, VA	82	82,135,000	148,945,000	231,080,000
San Francisco, Oakland, CA	66	89,775,000	113,210,000	202,985,000
Detroit, MI	69	74,520,000	125,480,000	200,000,000
Houston, TX	66	64,120,000	86,120,000	150,240,000
Boston, MA	57	38,435,000	97,980,000	136,415,000
Atlanta, GA	69	63,315,000	69,645,000	132,960,000
Dallas, TX	63	41,515,000	66,390,000	109,905,000

Source: Texas Transportation Institute Texas A&M University

Stress Acted Out

When traveling in stop and go traffic it is normal to get frustrated and angry as your mind crosses the line of common sense. The driver has a deep chronic sense or state of insecurity and dissatisfaction arising from human involved problems that stimulate an action. The driver arrives at a state where there is no respect for the person driving the vehicle in front and gets angry at everything, but why the driver immediately in front of their car? He or she is frustrated like others.

The drivers are angry because it is blocking the vehicle's forward movements. The driver makes a move to relieve some frustrations on the only thing he or she can to make a statement to try and satify their derived instinct. As an alternate, the person could park the vehicle on the side of the roadway and walk ahead to find the first car in that row that is causing it to stop its forward movement since all other cars are behind it. There are drivers that have shot other drivers, broke their windshields, and traveled close behind to upset them. Anything that will unconsciously trigger the system and fulfill their desire. Even animals react differently.

We are below animals at certain times when we are driven to make a decision saturated with anger. Chimpanzees share, mediate, reconcile, and other times they groom each other. Humans have developed the ability to reason abstractly and broaden their motions of who belongs to their tribe. It is an immediate reaction to a change in the environment.

The rough walls of the Grand Canyon can also inspire a transformation or transforming feeling of beings in the presence of something greater than individuals.

Many Americans drivers believe that road rage runs rampant in suburban areas. Their frustration in congested areas will add to aggressive driving. We all have been sitting in our vehicles waiting for traffic to move or making long detours because of road construction. Drivers often call it frustrating, transportation officials have a more formal name for it, road user cost and the Texas Department of Transportation is taking steps to incorporate it into recover cost for construction activities.

Hypothetically, if the amount of wasted time in congestion begins at 76 hours a year and continues in increments to 114 hours per year after 35 years, the amount of lost time for that person is 3,443 hours just sitting in traffic because of congestion only. That's and average of 43 two week vacations total over that period of time. This hypothetical exercise is used to give the reader a better understanding of what lost time in congestion means.

Wasted Fuel - Take A Train

These measures expressed the extra fuel consumed due to congestion only in a ratio with the number of eligible drivers in the urban area. It is the fuel lost for inefficient operation of the vehicle like stop and go, road congestion, paying tolls, violations that risk accidents, and lane changing. Included are some ways motorists illustrate that they value their travel time. The fuel used cannot be made better by carpool/bus, increase lanes, and coordinated traffic signals. A new way has to start by less use of highways and airplanes when riding short distances that should be on trains.

Los Angeles eligible driver wasted 110 gallons per year, but because of the size of Los Angeles it had the greatest amount of wasted fuel in 1996 and the total was 984 million gallons. Washington, DCs eligible driver wasted 118 gallons per year, but the size of the District decreased the total amount wasted.

In all of the 70 urban areas studied, over 6.7 billion gallons of fuel was wasted because of traffic congestion. This is the equivalent of 134 fully-loaded super tankers of 670,000 gasoline tank trucks loaded with gasoline. Three urban areas used more than 100 gallons of wasted fuel per driver in 1996: Los Angeles, Washington. DC., and Atlanta. GA. One of the small cities, Harrisburg, PA used 72 gallons per driver.

To further emphasize our vehicles thirst for gasoline, in 1982, approximately 2.7 billion gallons of fuel were wasted due to congestion. This equates to about 54 fully-loaded supertankers or 270,000 tank trucks loaded with gasoline. In 1982, only 16 urban areas had more than 36 gallons per eligible driver of wasted fuel per year which is equivalent to about 3 vehicle tanks per year. See table 1.5 for the annual wasted fuel per eligible driver and per capita.

Table 1.5

Annual Wasted Fuel Consumed per Driver and Total Annual Amount Consumed Per City Due to Traffic Congestion in 1996

Urban Area	Annual Gallons Wasted Per Driver	Annual Total Gallons Wasted per City		
		Recurring	Incident	Total
Los Angeles, CA	110	453,000,000	531,000,000	984,000,000
New York, NY-NE, NY	63	305,000,000	578,000,000	883,000,000
Chicago, IL NW, In	60	166,000,000	192,000,000	358,000,000
Washington, DC-MD-VA	118	118,000,000	215,000,000	333,000,000
San Francisco-Oakland, CA	98	133,000,000	168,000,000	301,000,000
Detroit, MI	99	106,000,000	179,000,000	285,000,000
Houston, TX	97	95,000,000	127,000,000	222,000,000
Boston, MA	81	55,000,000	141,000,000	196,000,000
Atlanta, GA	102	93,000,000	103,000,000	196,000,000

Source: Texas Transportation Institute Texas A&M University

Most people do not consider the wasted fuel used based only on congestion which cannot be recycled. The total amount includes the recurring events and the incidents encountered on the roadways during peak hours. Recurring events are delays relative to traffic per lane, changing lanes, and required traffic speeds. Incidents are roadway vehicle breakdowns and vehicle crashes.

Recurring and incidents are combined based on the number of drivers in the urban areas listed. Large urban areas with many drivers consume more wasted gasoline than smaller areas even though the gallons per person does not show a wide margin. The quantities of the figures in the table are shown in full values to underline the amount of gasoline wasted only because of congestion. A new train would greatly reduce the amount lost and provide a better way of travel with shorter trip times.

The annual wasted fuel per driver in Chicago, IL, NW-IN has the lowest. It could be because of the wide streets and longer city blocks that creates lower fuel consumed per driver compared to the size of the city for total gallons consumed.

The number of gallons of wasted fuel for nearly all cities listed except two are in close proximity. This indicates that all urban areas listed is heavily congested requardless of the size of the urban areas.

See Table 1.5A for a comparison of the years 1996 and 2000.

Table 1.5A

Annual Losses per Driver in 1996 and 2000 Due To Congestion

Urban Area	Congestion Cost		Hours of Delay		Wasted In	Fuel Gallons
	1996	2000	1996	2000	1996	2000
Los Angeles, CA	$1,205	$2,510	76	136	110	204
Chicago, IL, NW, IN	$670	$1,235	42	67	60	104
Washington, DC. MD, VA	$1,290	$1,595	82	84	118	136
San Francisco, Oakland, CA	$1,055	$1,770	66	92	98	149
Detroit, MI	$1,095	$1,030	69	55	99	90
Houston, TX	$1,055	$1,410	66	75	97	123
Boston, MA	$900	$1,255	57	67	81	107
Atlanta, GA	$1,095	$1,350	69	70	102	119
Dallas-Fort Worth, TX	$1,015	$1,390	63	74	72	120
New York NY-Northeastern NJ	$705	$1,400	44	73	63	120

Source: Texas Transporation Institute Texas A&M University, 2002

Condition of Bridges We Drive On

The condition of roadways and bridges are part of the cost for congestion, time, and delays. In January 2001 on Route 128 in Massachusetts, a heavily traveled and popular road used for commuting everyday caused a problem. Over a bridge at 11 a.m., a three by four foot hole appeared in a high speed lane and over twenty vehicles had their tires damaged and probably needed front end alignment after hitting the edges. Looking at the large hole, one could see small steel beams attached to the concrete road surface over top of the bridge. Also in view were ends laying on the floor of the bridge that were once small steel beams. They showed the thin metal ends had rusted. It was constructed in 1955 and was considered structurally deficient with a poor rating. The pothole was blamed on the wild temperature fluctuations that had occurred lately which is a poor excuse. A new design will not be installed until 2003 as repair of more bridges and roads will be needed and required.

Federal records showed that more than half the bridges in Massachusetts and Rhode Island are to weak, displapidated, and to overburdened for current traffic travel. Some of the deficient bridges are in danger of collapsing, though there have been few recent incidents. More than 10 Highway-Department bridges are structural deficient in Massachusetts, and the number of bridges fitting that category grows larger every "month" for repair. Even if the funds were available, it requires a large number of workers, inspectors, time for repair, and a lot of congestion. Even with the massive amount of work going on in Boston, bridges and local highways have been crumbing and getting weaker. In Tennessee a new bridge being built collapsed before it was finished and twisted like a piece of licorice candy.

See table 1.6 for bridge inventory.

Table 1.6

Bridge Inventory-Total Deficient: 1999 to 2000

States	No of Bridges	Deficient & Obsolete	Funct-ionally Obsolete	States	No of Bridges	Deficient & Obsolete	Funct-ionally Obsolete
Total							
1999	585,542	170,050	81,900				
2000	587,755	167,993	80,887				
AL	15,035	5,053	2,207	NB	15,507	4477	1,717
Alaska	1,409	400	232	NV	1,424	216	148
AZ	6,714	696	500	NH	2,348	799	410
AK	12,451	3,500	2,018	NJ	6,350	2,367	1,402
CA	23,672	6,790	4,332	NM	3,694	673	359
CO	7,977	1,440	853	NY	17,387	7,038	3,608
CT	4,178	1,278	907	NC	16,822	5,326	2,720
DL	824	131	78	ND	4,517	1,174	281
FL	11,181	2,227	916	OH	27,902	7,269	3,797
GA	14,382	3,712	1,938	OK	22,799	9,497	1,444
Hawaii	1,066	550	349	OR	7,257	1,642	1,320
ID	4032	752	435	PA	22,052	9,501	4,906
IL	25,497	4961	2,140	P Rica	2,068	1,011	755
IN	18,002	4,445	1,945	RI	747	375	188
IW	24,632	7,124	2,116	SC	9,064	1,878	869
KS	25,720	6,651	3,118	SD	6,032	1,802	3,064
KT	13,374	4072	2,879	TN	19,404	4954	3,064
LA	13,485	4706	2,184	TX	47,888	10,378	7,066
ME	2,360	873	498	UT	2,750	604	245
MD	4,965	1,445	1,005	VT	2,703	1,012	444
MA	4953	2,480	1,775	VA	12,710	3,524	2,287
MI	10,581	3,517	1,336	WA	7,876	2,103	1,523
MN	12,811	1,882	604	WV	6,730	2,791	1,586
MS	16,672	5,144	1,293	WS	1,318	2,677	885
MO	23,388	9,058	2,697	WY	3,110	662	885
MT	4,981	1,194	569	WA, DC	250	182	134

Bridges are functionally obsolete if their load carrying capacity and road alignment no longer meet the criteria for the bridge systems.

Source: US Federal Highway Administration, Office of Bridge Technology.

Plywood is underneath the 62 year old Calvin Coolidge bridge in Massachusetts to prevent pieces from the crumbling deck from hitting boaters on the Connecticut river underneath. (nothing was said about catching cars) When holes are patched, the primary patching falls through the bridge. More than 40,000 vehicles per day cross the bridge that was built years ago to carry 10,000 vehicles daily. It is one of the 799 structurally deficient bridges across the state and some of the bridges are on the busiest Interstate highways, and a Federal highway officials said 1,775 are considered to be inadequate for traffic. A ramp bridge carrying traffic to Interstate 90 was closed because of its condition and it has been in need of immediate repairs for years.

Massachusetts bridges are the third worst in the US. One out of every seven is structurally deficient. New Hampshire bridges are as outdated as the state laws that refer to the weight of wagons and cattle that could cross safely. The latest federal data said 34 percent of the state's bridges are deficient, and 799 are structurally obsolete and too narrow or weak to handle current traffic loads. The study showed that New Hampshire and Massachusetts were the worst in the nationwide survey. The government rated 167,993 of 587,755 bridges as deficient in August of 2000. That is over 1/4 of the total number of bridges.

Many spans have falling concrete and weak supports across the country, even through the government has spent billions on repairs for the last few years. The computer analysis found that more than one quarter of the bridges nationwide showed problems, but Rhode Island, New Hampshire, Hawaii, and Massachusetts has the worst. The bridges across the country were build years ago and have not been thoroughly checked or repaired. When the tracks were being reworked for the Acela Amtrak, some bridges were built in the late 1800s.

Because repair of bridges has been ignored in the 60s, 70s, and early 80s, there is a large backlog said Senator Stanley Rosenberg, and there are so many bridges that need immediate repair. "The one's that causes accidents will be repaired first." Robin Crosbie Hadley, town administrator said, businesses are being affected also. Since large sums of money is needed, $120 million has been committed to repair 69 bridges. In New Hampshire the federal data includes only the 2,348 bridges eligible for federal funds, but there are 1,250 more structures the state classifies as bridges that need repair. Powelson said that typical bridges last approximately 50 years, but the new materials used now will cause them to last longer.

In the last of May 2002, a bridge column of a main lane highway was hit by a barge in Tulsa, Oklahoma and fourteen travelers fell from the highway into the water and were killed. More than 7,400 bridges in Oklahoma are in such poor condition that they need to be replaced according to the Tulsa World. Eighteen bridges over rivers and lakes where navigation permits are required, including one over the Verdigris River where barges pass have no protection on their piers.

More than 1,800 bridges over navigable waterways have no pier proterction and those that do have protection is in deteriorating condition records show.

Annual Highway Funds We Pay per State

The "highest disbursement of funds" for highways was in California with and estimated cost in 1997 of $6.219 billion ($6,219,000,000) for that year. That is the amount of money spent in only one state. The repairs cause a wide margin of congestion, delays, and wasted fuel. Table 1.7 has the disbursement of state highway funds per state from 1990 to 1997. The total estimated amount the US paid for 1997 was $72 billion.

Table 1.7

Disbursement of State Highway Funds by State 1990 to 1997 ($667 represents $667,000,000. Comprises disbursement from current revenues includes transactions by state toll authorities. Excludes amounts allocated for collection expenses, non-highway purposes, and bonds redeemed by refunding)

State	1990	1995	1997	State	1990	1995	1997
KS	$667	$1,019	$1,087	ND	$189	$270	$326
KY	1,008	1,342	1,331	OH	2,271	2,637	2,940
LA	923	1,195	1,189	OK	827	828	867
ME	332	379	474	OR	765	888	992
MD	1,484	1,289	1,489	PA	2,885	3,153	3,764
MA	1,055	2,501	3,287	RI	214	290	225
MI	1,526	1,974	2,100	SC	585	666	741
MN	1,228	1,210	1,450	SD	332	286	349
MS	529	662	809	TN	1,174	1,230	1,351
MO	937	1,313	1,492	TX	3,001	3,593	4,253
MT	302	388	379	UT	355	431	802
NE	449	578	611	VT	186	194	213
NV	309	484	431	VA	1,874	2,107	2,358
NH	298	328	360	WA	1,251	1,842	1,851
NJ	1,831	2,102	2,247	WV	650	781	940
NM	409	535	546	WI	979	1,252	1,354
WY	297	272	284	NC	1,428	1,871	2,099

1997 US total $72,000,000,000

US Highway Administration, Highway Statistics

Chapter 2: Winglock-Security Checks & Pretzels

Some Causes of Delays

Before the September 11, 2001 attack, winglock, gridlock, airport delays, cancellation, and weather uncertainties were something that we accepted. Will winglock, limited runways, long lines at ticket counters, check through metal detectors, people waiting in airports, bad weather, long walks to airport gates, and long waits before boarding airplanes get worst? Weather is always unpredictable and has a significant role in determining how many and how long the delays will be. Weather delays and the length of time of the delays depend on weather conditions at the airport you are in, and the weather and conditions at or near the airport where the plane is scheduled to land. If weather is bad where your connecting flight lands, there may be another delay. The disturbing part is, no ones knows how long the delays will be. There is a cold notification that your flight has been canceled and you receive that information from a big television screen where you stand and look up.

The level of service is what the traveler is interested in. Waiting time, reliability, traveling time, comfort, safety, and security are examples of level of service that is relevant to the travelers. They are also not just interested in going from one airport to another airport, but are interested in going from an origin to a destination. That involves traveling to the airport, getting their ticket, checking their bags, passing through the checking device, flying to a second airport at the destination city, picking up their bags and traveling to their destination. This is called trip time.

This book emphasize access to airports by rail which the European airports have been using for years. In Hartsfield Airport in Atlanta, GA you get off of the plane, get on a train or subway without even leaving the terminal. Plane to train or train to plane.

With so many airlines overbooking, cancellations will continue, and during holidays in 2000 there were a record number of people waiting to fly. One of the primary causes of packed tarmacs was a booming economy and the added short distance flights. In 1978, the airlines carried 275 million people. In 1999, they carried more than 650 million. The Air Transport Association said, during the Christmas holidays in the year of 2000, 39 million people were flying over a three week period.

The antiquated traffic control systems are trying to work with flights leaving and landing at airports that are already overcrowded and continuing to get worst. The FAA abandoned the advanced automatic system that was being developed in 1999 after spending $2.9 billion. It would not have solved the problems, but the new systems could have provided a better quality of service.

Security Checks at Logan Before Terrorist Attack

Watchdog agencies and presidential commissions warned lapses in the security system could have catastrophic consequence, but efforts to remedy the problems had been frustrated repeatedly by cost-conscious airlines that paid for their security employees. The airlines would take the passengers money, but did not consider passenger safety as a high and necessary priority. It was very easy for the managers of the airlines to realize, if a terrorist passed the checkpoint with a bomb that later blew up their airplane, the cost in lives and monetary lost would be tremendous. The cost alone would be much larger than the amounts saved on laxed security over many years.

Vincent was an employee at Logan Airport and said, "we would not have been in this situation if the airlines had not fought the things we were recommending." The airlines who was responsible for the cost of most airport security procedures, continued to use their political power to frustrate FAA regulators. Even when the FAA aggressively attacked them, the airlines often persuade key members of Congress to intervene on their behalf. As a reward for their selfish attitudes after the terrorist attack, the government gave all airlines money to cover their losses in addition to the money they had knowingly saved on poor security systems.

Expensive bomb-detecting machines were often of little value because the pool of workers were underpaid and inadequately trained to operate the sophisticated equipment. Workers left the security jobs and received better pay at airport fast-food concessions stands, given stock options, and other benefits. The employment turnover was very high and those that worked at security usually worked two jobs because of necessity.

Most passengers did not know other security measures were supposed to be operating to provide safety. Being concern for security, Joseph Lawless was a Passport Director for public safety in 1994 and consulted the French security officials after the 1994 hijacking of the Air France plane. He started a $1 million a year program called, LASER, (Logan Airport Security Enhancement and Review) in 1997. One of the services provided was a supervisor and four or five troopers to patrol various areas. The idea was to saturate different parts of the airport, but with that number of troopers available, it was impossible. Some of the duties were to write violations, check identification of individuals and vehicles by setting up roadblocks, and check for unsecured doors. The troopers were to be able to assemble a team that could be deployed to respond to security emergencies, but how large was the team?

A wage for a security worker was $9.24 per hour to screen passengers at the L A International Airport checkpoint overseen by Delta Air Lines. The worker said there was intense pressure to move passengers through security at a fast pace. Sometimes supervisors overseeing checkpoints were forced to open another x-ray machine and metal detector with no additional staff for help.

At Logan and other airports, facility managers and airlines pushed subcontractors to quicken the pace at checkpoints. Last February in 2001, Logan's managers, Massport, and the Massachusetts Port Authority urged airlines to speed the movement of passengers throughout the system to ensure that waits would not exceed five minutes. A checkpoint worker said, we were under constant pressure from the airlines if there were lines at a security checkpoint. Safety was not their prime interest.

Moral was so low the average employee at Logan International Airport stayed on the job less than six months and this was true in a large number of airports. The results were, ill-trained security personnel often missed contraband items. Brian Sullivan, who retired early in 2001 as an FAA special agent said, he and other agents frequently slipped handguns and dummy bombs through security at major airports. One team slipped a rifle through the system.

Between 1999 and 2000, FAA agents were able to violate security sixty times by boarding unattended airplanes, entering unlocked doors that should have been locked, sneaked behind security guards, and secured access to restricted baggage and ramp areas. Those areas were required to be controlled by private security companies the airlines hired. Each airline hired their on security personnel and those areas were to be controlled by them sympathetic to the airlines.

In July 2001, test were reviewed by Logan Airlines Managers Council that represented carriers at the airport. State Police were to use security monitoring for a week and was ready to begin the program. Airline managers were very vocal in objecting to any testing by Massport. They were worried, not about the success of the test, but who would have access to the results of the tests and whether it would be shared with the FAA.

A committee of airline executives strenuously objected to Massport's proposal to use undercover state troopers to sneak weapons through checkpoints to test for security weakness.

Over $700,000 in fines was levied at Logan and with airlines lobbying, usually pennies were paid on dollars. The total amount paid for security breaches: $205,000 by Delta Airlines, $134,000 by US Airways, $117,000 by American, $110,000 by Continental, and $56,000 by United Airlines. The money collected could have been used in any number of ways.

Top security official, Michael Canavan, told the FAA regional officials not to fine airlines for security violations if it appeared "they intended to" correct their security violations. If the company believed security personnel had implemented a permanent fix that would solve the problem, do not expect us to impose a civil penalty against the party for "unaggravated" violations. Unaggravated violations can be interpreted as an item to make it worse or more serious. "How do you make a bomb more serious."

Paul Hudson, executive director of the Aviation Consumer Action Project at Logan, a non-profit watch dog group said in an interview, that he could not think of one thing that the airlines had proposed to enhance security, but I can think of many things they have done to inhibit it. When things occurred that indicated a need for corrective action, the proposals were refused, delayed, and watered down with no effect.

Security Checks After Terrorist Attack

After the terrorist attack in September 2001, Massport ordered State Police to monitor the same security checks the airlines had blocked. Carter Bibbey was the manager of the security employees that provided security for American Airlines. For the safety of errors and a better safety record for his security force, he did not want the checkpoint screeners to be forced to detect test weapons that were different than the standard test items the FAA used to check the quality of work of their screeners.

The manager of an Aviation Services said, his company did not want his employees to test items designed to help the screeners fail. He wanted the test to use objects screeners were more accustom to spotting. That's covering your company's safety record with no thoughts of doing a quality job and protecting the safety of passengers.

The trip time increased with no assurance of how much extra time would be required at the beginning and ending of the flight. The ticket agents suggested you arrive at the airport at least two to three hours before boarding time requiring the passenger to leave earlier getting to the airport.

The attendant at the check point had any number of uniformed police and federal officers standing by, but the attendant still did not like to provoke passengers that did not want their suitcases searched in view of other passengers behind them. Women were taken to a private area and the contents of their purse checked. If a male passenger had emptied all of his pockets and was wearing a metal belt buckle, the buzzer kept sounding when he walked through the metal detector. The antendant would scan his middle section and declare it was the belt buckle and clear the passenger. A gun could have been carried under the belt buckle inside his pants. However, if an attendant was suspicious of a man, he would be checked from head to foot with his shoes off.

After the passenger or passengers were cleared, they walked to the proper terminal, sat and waited for boarding time after arriving 3-1/2 plus hours before flight time.

Other added security measures were trash cans full or not were required to be emptied into locked garbage chutes once per hour. Plastic knives over four inches long are considered contraband and were not permitted at concession stands that could cause problems while eating.

Before checked bags were put on board the airplane from another part of the terminal, a few were opened and the neat orderly fashion of the contents were disturbed as a hand passes under the material, around the sides, and in the middle of the contents. Completion, it could resemble a container of clothes ready for the washing machine and if the top was difficult to close, pressure was applied by any methods to close the bag.

Laxed Security continued and the reason the national airport security system was so vulnerable before the terrorist attack, the FAA permitted passengers to carry four inches knives to please passengers because so many people carried them. A week after the terrorist attack when security was suppose to be better, a passenger went through Logan's International Airport with a corkscrew in the bottom of a carry-on-bag. When he deplaned, the security at another airport checked his bag on their X-ray machine and removed it. A passenger at Logan International had his bags inspected at a checkpoint and the security person allowed him to carry a pair of scissors on board. When the bags were checked after he landed in Canada, the items were noticed and confiscated.

Passengers leaving O'Hare International Airport in Chicago and Baltimore-Washington International Airport were allowed to carry nail files, hair shears, and an army knife on board an airplane. Senator Bill Nelson, a Florida Democrat, said undercover sheriffs deputies smuggled a blade and other potential weapons through checkpoints at Fort Lauderdale-Hollywood International Airport a few days after the terrorist attacks. Harry Petrie of London said he walked through the metal detector at Logan with a cigarette lighter in his breast pocket of his shirt.

A frequent rider arrived at Logan Airport September 30, walked from his car at the airport, and continued freely walking to the US Airways gate at Terminal B. He did not even see anyone that looked liked a security person and this was a few days after the bold terrorist attack and after the President informed all people under him and told the public that strict safety procedures would be followed. When the serious error was discovered, safety officials emptied the terminal and required all passengers to pass through security even though a device could have already been hidden in some location.

In September 2001, Virginia Buckingham said undercover State Police officers had smuggled a pocket full of bullets and a folding knife past airport security checkpoints. Airlines were not concern about safety, yet this government is giving large sums of money to help them financially. If they get rewarded for unsafe practices and negligence that could affect any number of lives, why should they be concern? They are getting paid for not doing their job.

Some Massport officials were saying the checkpoints should be controlled by the federal government and the airlines relieved of the responsibility of hiring a low bidding security company. After seeing security officers standing around talking and undertrained checkers with a complacent attitude, they should be removed. The equipment cannot be blamed since other airports discovered items that were not found in some US Airports and apparently the X-ray equipment was the same quality. All security systems should be operated by the government or under one manager that has an attitude of doing a security job the way it should be based on training, benefits, and promotions. Because there are other person's at the checkpoints does not mean security is better. It is the quality of service that person exhibits.

Continued Poor Security Checks by Argenbright Company

A company named Argenbright provided security at Logan International airport and 13 others nationwide was one of the nation's largest airport passenger screening companies. The FAA administration and inspector general of the US Department of Transportation launched an investigation of the company after a US attorney in Philadelphia charged that the Atlanta based company continued to hire screeners without appropriate background checks or training.

The company also hired employees on probation, ones that had been convicted, illegal aliens, and failed to train them. One employee at Seattle-Tacoma International was charged with illegal possession of a hand gun and screeners at Dallas-Fort Worth International were working illegally in the United States. Seven out of 20 screeners were tested for screening skills at Washington Dallas International and could not past a required test that should have disqualified them before being employed. He also hired workers without fingerprinting and criminal history checks.

He paid $1 million in fines in 2000 and was put on three years' probation for falsifying employee records, lying to federal investigators, and failing to conduct criminal background checks. US

Attorney Patrick L. Meehan filed suit against Argenbright for widespread violations.

With his negative attitude he filed a petition in United States District Court in Philadelphia seeking to revoke his probation. Here is a company or man that has been put on probation, fined $1 million dollars, and broke all federal laws over years of service that was continually providing a security service that could contribute to more terrorist attacks. Who is responsible and did he have lobbyist working for him?

Argenbright Security Inc., November 6, 2000, permitted a man at O'Hare International Airport to pass through a screening with knives, stun gun, and pepper spray. At another checkpoint he was stopped with two pocket knives and his baggage contained two long bladed knives. Seven security workers and three supervisors were suspended. Nothing was said about the security company. He probably was only fined again.

As long as there are security companies like this one and passengers brave enough to carry weapons when they board a plane, there will be no security that is dependable. Until the responsibility of security is removed from airlines and all security companies and their employees removed, passenger security will not be enforced.

The hijackers armed with plain box cutters might just as well have slipped heavy weaponry aboard. Most of the airlines that paid millions of dollars lobbying to prevent new or widening security efficiency, now have their hands out for financial help. Approximately 138,000 employees will lose their jobs with nine airlines, and the airlines have said, separation packages would not be financially feasible. That many airlines on the ground and that many unemployed will cause a rippling affect on just about everything.

The airlines were still lobbying Congress for over $24 billion, not millions. Delta Air Lines Inc. said the industries total losses would be $18 billion. Transportation Secretary Norman Minuets said, he would make a proposal for $250 million a day to the airlines after the terrorist tragedy. The amount paid to each airline was based on the number of miles they flew. The question raised, why should the government save or try to save a company or companies that were going bankrupt before the tragedy? Some airlines were already hurting because of the slowing economy and competition.

Congress allotted $5 billion for financial losses to the airlines. Already $2.4 billion have been given to the airlines including $391 million to United Airlines, and $327 million to Delta Airlines.

Lobbying In Washington

A normal way of thinking would be that the airlines welcomed security checks. They have hired an army of lobbyists and spent millions of dollars to prevent tighter security checks. Nine top line airlines and their trade group have given $16 million in political constibutions since 1991. Since 1997, they have given $63 million for lobbying efforts on our Capitol Hill.

Harshbarger, the former Massachusetts attorney general said, that people should understand that the airline industry has been more concerned with it's bottom line than about safety and security for the public. The airlines bravely continues to insist that its economic security is more important than public safety and passenger safety and the interests of its own employees. The September attack had no affect on their thinking.

President Bush signed into law November 19, 2001 new baggage-screening requirements, and the airlines tried to delay it. The airlines have fought to remove or weaken a bag-matching measure stating it will lead to increase delays and cost too much to implement. Bag matching is where every piece of luggage is positively matched with a passenger which is something that should already be required. Anyone can pick up a bag and walk out of the airport without even anyone looking at that person.

In 1997, the Federal Aviation Administration conducted a two-week test of bag matching on 8,000 flights and the study found that

14 percent of flights would experience delays an average of "seven minutes" and the system would cost 40 cents per passenger. Seven minutes could be shortened by getting the bags at the pickup point earlier.

Travelers were in the popular habit of flying and were driven to fly because they had been conditioned. A radical change was needed and has been needed for years for travelers since policy makers do not see the problems. There was a need to break the mental mold, compare the trip time, and make a simple comparative analysis of the two modes of traveling, flying or riding the train for distances of at least 400 miles.

The airlines have 210 lobbyists that are some of the most well-connected people in Washington. Included in that group is Wendell Ford, D-Kentucky, Bob Packwood, R-Oregon, Linda Daschle, a former FAA official and wife of Senate Majority leader Tom Daschle, D-South Dakota, and former Senators Dale Bumper, D-Arizona. The total number of lobbyists are 210.

US Representative James L. Oberstar, Democrat of Minnesota, discovered this in 1990 when he championed legislation in the aftermath of the Pan Am 103 explosion over Lockerbie, Scotland. He proposed a ten year background investigation for all airport security workers. The airlines did not like the cost and wanted such a check only when there was a year long gap in employment. The proposal was delayed and weakened.

TWA flight 800 departed Kennedy Airport in New York off Long Island and an explosion tore the airplane apart killing everyone on board. In the summer of 1996, the Presidential Commission issued a report containing numbers of recommendations to enhanced security and safety. The airline industry used its leverage on the FAA to delay or dilute many recommendations, including new training for airport screeners. The expensive machinery used for detection is often operated by security workers with insufficient training.

In 2000, the performance of present airport security screeners were unsatisfactory in detecting contraband items like handguns. The FAA report in 1999 pinpointed Logan International as one of many major airports with serious security flaws. During one two-year period in the late 1990s, Massport paid $178,000 in fines for security violations that could have been used for better security.

That prompted Vice President Gore's Commission, even in its watered-down final report in February 1997, to urge a substantial increase in standards, training, pay, and advancement opportunities for airport security. The airlines that pay the security bills, fought the change.

Vincent, the former FAA security chief said, airlines began a vigorous lobbying campaign aimed at the White House. Two weeks later, Vice President Gore retreated from the proposal in a letter to Carol B. Hallett, the president of The Air Transport Association. The day after Gore's letter, TWA donated $40,000 to the Democratic National Committee. The time of the presidential election, other airlines gave large donations to Democratic Party Committees: $265,000 from American Airlines, $120,000 from Delta Air Lines, $115,000 from United Air Lines, and $87,000 from Northwest. Airlines that totaled $587,000. Over the preceding 10 week period, the airlines gave the Democrats half that sum.

Only now after the terrorist attack are the recommendations of the Gore Commission being seriously considered. Hudson said, there is a virtual interlock between the airline industry, the Transportation Department, and the FAA. The aviation industry spends over $20 million a year to get their way in Washington, and they do. I have never seen a serious instance in which they have not.

Mary Schiavo, a former FAA inspector general said, she believes the contributions helped ensure that the airlines avoided expensive new requirements, such as baggage match. Vincent, the former FAA chief, holds the same view. All Washington's major players share responsibilities for the airport security system that was badly compromised. Jenkins said, I do not think the government did enough for safety.

The Domino Effect In Unemployment

The dramatic drop in air travel after the terrorist attack was hurting businesses at all levels of the economy in a rapid slowdown that analyst predicted would lead to hundreds of thousands of layoffs. Major airlines planned to lay off about 100,000 workers, and jet maker Boeing advertised cutting 30,000. The full economic impact of the air travel slowdown is still unwinding, and economists say job and revenue losses are a moving target. Estimated effects would lead to a lost of 1.5 million jobs in all types of businesses across the country over the next six months. About 250,000 will be laid off by airlines, jet manufacturers, and other aviation subcontractors, David Wyss, Standard & Poor's chief economists said. Surly prospects for Boeing's continued sales of airplanes could not be estimated with any confidence, but why lay off 30,000 employees unless the company had already seen financial problems with work around the clock schedules?

This was a severe downturn in the economy. When one domino went over, they all started to fall. Overseas airlines joined their American counterparts and began to make cuts with British Airways, the largest European carrier, announcing 7,000 layoffs, and our industry has asked for billions of dollars for a federal bale out in the United States or several companies could go bankrupt.

The ripple effects caused problems because those companies contract so much work. When you see large layoffs inside Boeing, you will see large layoffs at their suppliers said Eric Johnson, professor at Dartmouth College's Tuck School of Management. Hertz Corp. owned by Ford Motor Company said its business had fallen 50 percent nationwide and 75 percent at Logan Airport. This included layoffs, furloughs, and reductions in the size of the rental fleet.

Large manufactures have a big backlog for new airplanes to be sold keeping more airplanes in the sky. As the old planes are reconfigured for freight, the total numbers will increase. Can we use the terrorist attack as a subconscious way to control the number of planes flying and a stimulant for business people and travelers to ride trains more as new faster trains are being built and funded by the government?

Hotels slumped to 40 percent affecting restaurants. General Electric Jet Engines which made 1,500 to 2,000 engines a year for commercial aircraft received calls from airlines that were delaying orders, and small business do not have room to shrink. The economic outlook for America was already on a downward trend, but the large numbers of new layoffs and the build up of reservists in our country will effects the economy even more.

Flying Before Terrorist Attack

After you boarded your plane at the airport, the short people and some senior citizens had trouble getting their bags in the overhead compartments. Passengers sat, buckled their seatbelts, and raised their seats to the secured position providing more knee room for the occupant seated behind. The steward or stewardess gave a demonstration on how to fasten a complicated seatbelt and how to operate the oxygen mask over your head while the seatbelt sign was still on.

When the plane was cleared to leave the loading dock, it slowly travels to the proper take off runway and waited before taking off. When cleared, it gained speed to reach the cruising altitude, and the steward or stewardess gave more orders. The Captain has turned off the seatbelt sign, even though the sign was not lit, and you are free to get up and walk not around, but in straight lines. The person sitting in front of you lets the seat back on your knees and this is the time you think about the basketball players if they do not fly first class. The Captain lets you know he is still flying the airplane by giving the needed information that we are flying at a certain altitude, the arrival time, and what the weather is like at the next airport landing.

While waiting for your unanticipated snack, you raise your seat to look out the small window to see whatever there is to see. This is the time you remember seeing a large well designed airplane sitting at the loading dock. The small windows looked like designed symbols between the lower part of the airplane and top to give a contrast.

The attendant pulls a small cart down the aisle while another one pushes. The one on your side voluntarily gives you a snack when you are reached. It is the smallest bag of bagels or pretzels made, but you do get a choice of a drink in a small container. The Captain communicates to everyone periodically and in rough weather the fasten seatbelt sign appears on a screen in front of you. As a safety factor, if you failed to read the sign or cannot read English, the attendant says, "the captain has turned on the seatbelt sign."

If making a connection with another airplane, as soon as you landed and entered the airport, there was usually an airport person standing at the off ramp telling you the gate number to proceed to catch your airplane or wait. Usually you had to walk a long distance, but for your convenience in some airports, there was a shuttle moving track that you stood on or there was a shuttle bus.

Deplaning and reaching the gate at your final destination, you walked through a packed concourse a long distance following the sign pointing to the baggage claim area. You find the right carousel, stand and wait until you hear a noise and see bags coming through a hole in the wall and entering another on the other side. Seldom does the hostess tell you the carousel where the baggage will be.

If someone is picking you up, the driver has already picked up a ticket for parking and attempted to locate a parking space in a crowded large parking lot on difference levels. The driver drives around until a space is spotted, but when it is reached, a small compact car has already parked in that spot.

After the vehicle is parked at another location, the driver walks the distance to the baggage areas and stand and wait until the passenger is in sight. You have already put a dollar and a half in a slot to rent a baggage cart to carry your bags in.

You and the driver remove the bags from the carousel and load them on the rented cart. With the other packs in your hands, you walk and the other person pushes the cart to the parked car. The driver loads the bags into the car, relocate the cart, and drives to the gate to pay the fee for parking.

Some passengers are required to get a shuttle from the baggage area. Passengers that had cars in the satellite parking carried their baggage to the correct location and waited until a shuttle bus appeared where they boarded with bags and rode to the parking lot.

You reached your final destination after hours of lost time. When you consider the time spent at the airport, the flight time, and the time to get to and from the airport, you are surprised at the amount of time lost.

Changes in Airline Amenities

Since our transportation in the skies did not have competition from the train or any other people moving systems, the public kept flying as the amenities of the trips were continually decreased. As late as the 1970s each passenger flying a certain distance or at certain times of the day received a full course delicious meal with additional liquids if the passenger wanted it. People on a restricted diet could call before the flight, request certain foods, and it would be served to that person on the airplane. Nearly all travelers anticipated the meals being served and that added to the enjoyment of the trip.

Looking at ways to spend less money, the airlines started serving a small bag of peanuts or bagels and a small cup of liquid. Now we get the smallest bag of bagels or pretzels made instead of peanuts.

The seat in front of the passenger provided a comfortable amount of leg room and the seats behind the bulkheads provided more leg room for a comfortable flight for even the over six foot person. Now on most airlines, when a person sitting in front of a six foot and over person, he can only let the seat back a certain distance. It stops moving backward when it rest on the passenger's knees sitting behind. The passenger seated behind the bulkhead is also cheated of leg room. The major difference, instead of looking at the head of the person in front of you, he or she looks at a big blank wall.

Airline business being good and seeing no competition for the growing number of flyers, the airlines raised the fares. To aid in keeping the airplane full, the airlines started over-booking so if any passengers canceled their flights or did not fly, the airlines could use flyers from the overbooked list. The airlines took another aggressive step for a just-in-case effort. If the passenger list did not contain enough passengers names to fill the airplane flying, the flight was canceled.

After the terrorist attack, fewer airlines were flying because of fewer passengers. Those that flew had to be at the air terminal hours before the airplane was scheduled to leave because of the new security procedures. There is talk of pilots and copilots carrying loaded guns and some attendants want to carry pepper spray or stun guns. Security people with guns will ride a few airplanes for emergency purposes, but will it really help?

One month later, US Airways shuttle from Logan Airport to Reagan National began 14 flights a day overloaded with passengers.

Chapter 3: The Airlines We Fly

Airplane Misses and Contract Delays

In June 1991, a small plane landed at Plant City Airport outside of Tampa. It had another plane on top of it two hundred feet in the air. The interlocked pair landed together without injury to any occupants aboard. Two jetliners nearly collided at 36,000 feet nearly seven miles up, carrying approximately 700 passengers. They avoided an in-flight collision in 2001. One of the planes dived quickly for safety from the other's path. Thirty five people were injured, three seriously, but it was a blessing both jetliners did not dive.

A transcript between air traffic controllers and pilots suggested the aircraft came as close as 200 feet. That is a little over 1/2 of a football field. The flight plan called for planes to pass each other with a distance of 2,000 feet or nearly 1/2 of a mile between them. On Japan's Semipublic Television Networks a passenger said, I have never seen a plane fly that close. I thought we were going to crash. In 2001, two airplanes at Logan Airport caused damage to each other while taxing.

A Boeing 747-400 carrying 411 passengers and 16 crew members had a near miss with a DC-10. The pilots of both planes reported that their collision warning devices failed, forcing them to take emergency measures. The warning device is set to sound 25 to 40 seconds before an imminent crash, a little over 1/2 of a minute. There should always be a redundant system for continuous service. When one device stops operating another automatically starts. With two planes going in the opposite directions at approximately 500 mph, each approached and passed each other at a high rate of speed, but what is the probability of two systems on both airplanes approaching each other being inoperative at the same time?

The busiest terminal in the US is Chicago's O'Hare International Airport. It is one big airport with more than "12 million" hours of passenger delays per year. The equivalent of 1,400 people standing idle around the clock all year, noted the Argonne Report. A number of airports have more than three million hours of passenger delays annually, and the delays are expected to double causing more airports to handle more than 160 percent of air traffic it was designed for.

Some of the things that are causing delays at airports no human person can do anything to alleviate. Winds gusting to 60 mph or over in certain directions of the runways caused cancellation of flights at a number of airports including Boston International. The delays were in addition to the snowing and snow on the ground in the Northeast and Midwest causing thousands of passengers to be stranded. One day LaGuradia Airport did not have a takeoff or landing for 90 minutes honoring the high cross-winds.

One of the other problems is labor disputes. In 2000, airline workers including pilots and mechanics, had a dispute about working overtime. With their contractual rights, it seems no one could do anything about the relations in the airline industry whether the passengers were frustrated or angry. Darryl Jenkins, the director of the Aviation Institute at George Washington University said, in the 1970s and 1980s, there were labor disputes, but this was the worst it has ever been. The airlines had high load factors (seats filled with paying passengers) causing the attendants that worked in the airplanes with passengers to feel they received benefits that were not comparable to benefits other airlines attendants were being paid.

They were working under a 75-year old Railway Labor Act that prevented most of the workers from striking even though their contract had expired. To prolong the situation, correct bargaining processes ended and went to the National Mediation Board that had the power to declare an impasse and order a 30 day cooling-off-period before the workers could strike. Because of the limited strike options, union slow downs were around busy travel periods as holidays to put pressures on the airlines. Delaying a contract can be advantageous because retroactive pay increases are negotiated and not mandatory, so delays can apply more pressure.

The Aircraft Mechanics Fraternal Association first proposal was in 2000 with an inflated 114 percent wage increase and a massive retroactive bonus. The National Mediation Board suspended talks until the union presented something more realistic. It is never ending because if one airline company employees get a raise, all other airline employees will seek matching wages called pattern bargains.

There is another problem said Dan Kasper, managing director of an economics consulting firm in Cambridge, MA. When union leaders agree to a new contract quickly, dissenters may be able to challenge them by saying too much was left on the table causing more time to be wasted. Kasper also said there is an incentive for union leaders to drag out negotiations. One way pressure was applied to Northwest Airline, 9,800 mechanics had a contract that should have changed in October 1996 rather than 2000. In the summer of 1998 an agreement was tentatively reached with the International Association of Machinists, but it was challenged by the Aircraft Mechanics Fraternal Association that caused not only a change in union leadership, but a change in unions. It did serve a purpose because time passed while the challenges were overturned before contract negotiations started again.

American Airlines flight attendants union announced in 2000, that it would push for a strike-authorization vote. They had been working without a contract for more than 2 years. The announcement was made by the Associations Professional Fight Attendants.

Delta Airlines canceled approximately 1,700 flights during the first 10 days of January in 2000. More than half of the delays were due to pilots being unavailable a Delta spokesman said. During the same year in 2000, Delta Air Lines appealed to a federal judge's refusal to force pilots to work overtime.

Travelers Sick of Crowded Airports and Delays

Last year in 2000 the nations commercial airlines experienced more delays and cancellations than any other time in history. Of course we had more people, more people traveling, more vehicles, and more congestion. To help, the Airline Industry Trade Association made an announcement that the formation of a coalition was designed to push runway construction around the nation. Boston Massport's executive director, Virginia Buckingham, was taking a leading role in that effort.

Soon afterward, the government came back with the release of a report by the Inspector General of The Department of Transportation on how poorly airlines had handled customer service issues. The Air Transport Association asked President Bush to make aviation a national priority and to speed up improvements in aviation infrastructure. It was seen by some as a defensive measure to blunt expected criticism from the inspector general's report.

Carol Hallett, president of the Air Transportation Association said, by spending $2.15 billion in five years instead of 10 years and implementing a navigation system based on global positioning satellites would be achieved more quickly. She called for hiring 1,000 more air traffic controllers at a cost of $200 million over five years.

The members of the newly formed coalition called Runways, believe the problems are not in air traffic control, but a shortage of pavement on the ground. They advocated runway construction to reduce the nation's chronic air travel delay problems according to a coalition statement. The attendants included the chief executives of American Airlines, Delta Airlines, United Airlines, as well as airport executives from Boston, Denver, Houston, Las Vegas, Memphis, Minneapolis, Phoenix, St. Louis, San Francisco, Seattle, and Washington, DC. Also included were executives of trade associations for the airlines, airports, and the United States Chamber of Commerce. Eleven airports, major airlines, and major US businesses were coming together to underscore building new runways at key airports was the only way to address the crisis in aviation, said Buckingham. They wanted to urge the Bush administration and Congress to make building runways a priority.

The real purpose was to convince the Federal Government that runways will have to be built at any cost and are the golden answer to delay problems. Anyone paying attention knows that is not the case and is poor thinking for spending money because it will not solve long range or short range problems. It is a way to flex more muscle to keep the public out of discussions about what happens in their communities. Why not more Supertrains like the Acela Amtrak, Maglev, and more up-date tracks?

Air traffic delays soared to a record in 2000 with late operations up 20 percent over 1999, the government said in 2001. In addition to more air traffic delays, The Transportation Department reported more consumer complaints about service for that year. LaGuradia was ranked as the most congested US airport in 2000 and the increased volume of flights caused more delays. Volume was responsible for 14 percent of all delays and was up 42 percent from 1999 the FAA said. It has been more than a year and the situation is not getting any better, said Kevin Mitchell, chairman of the Business Travel Coalition. He said, about 75 percent of the delays affected business travelers who are deeply frustrated.

Table 3.1 list on time arrivals for airlines from 1995 through 1999.

Table 3.1

Airlines On-Time Arrivals 1995 to 1999
(percent based on gate arrival times for domestic flights. A flight is on time if less than 15 minutes after schedule. Canceled and diverted flights are considered late)

Airline	1995	1996	1997	1998	1999
Northwest	80.7	76.6	74.7	70.6	75.2
Southwest	82.3	81.8	81.9	80.8	80.2
TWA	74.3	68.5	80.2	78.3	75.8
Delta	76.2	71.2	74.1	79.6	77.1
Continental	79.5	76.6	78.2	77.3	78.3
US Airways	79.8	75.7	80.1	78.9	68.5
American West	77.6	70.8	77.5	68.5	74.1
United	77.7	73.8	75.9	73.8	74.6
American	77.5	72.2	79.1	80.1	70.4
Average	78.1	74.5	77.7	77.2	74.8

Source: Office of General Counsel, U.S. Department of Transportation

In the Massachusetts area, business men were taking taxis to New York from Boston because of delays and missed meeting. Taxis delivers them to their meeting locations and if three or more business men take a taxi, the cost is very reasonable with only traffic delays. There are vehicles that just advertise and carry passengers to New York.

There were over 29,000 air traffic operations delayed 15 minutes or more in October 2000, more than 34,000 in November, and more recorded in December the FAA said. For that year, there were

450,289 total delays, up more than 20 percent from 1999. Approximate 68 percent of the late flights were attributed to bad weather. Thirty percent of all delays due to increased flight volume was the result of congestion at LaGuardia Airport in New York.

Transportation Secretary Norman Minutia predicted that delays probably would get worse in 2001. Improving the nation's air traffic system and finding ways to boost capacity at airports to meet demand are top priorities. The industry also expressed frustration with delays saying, the federal government needs to address an overburdened air traffic control system. Without intervention, the problems will continue to grow, particularly leading to the summer travel season said Michael Wascom, spokesman for the Air Transport Association, the industry's chief lobbying group. The group urged the Bush administration in 2001 to fight delays with $4.8 billion in accelerated spending on a satellite navigation system and hiring more air traffic controllers.

A report from the Department of Transportation discovered that when inspectors looked at delayed flights, 21 percent of the time airline flights information showed flights were on time when they were delayed at least 20 minutes. Airlines failed to inform passengers adequately about the delays and cancellations that plague the nation's aviation system.

Announcements about flight delay status at gates were made only 66 percent of the time and when they were made, they were accurate 57 percent of that time. In the year of 2000, the Department of Transportation said, one-in-four flights were delayed, canceled, or diverted. The airlines has to reduce over-scheduling also.

Passengers also criticize the airlines for not identifying chronic delayed flights. There is also a need to clarify their policies on how to treat passengers who are stranded overnight because of delays and cancellations. Passengers bumped from a flight are treated differently from those that are bumped and take the next flight.

Data collected by the Transportation Department in 2001 said:

1. The consumer wants to be treated with more respect and receive more reliable service.
2. Passengers being bumped from airlines against their wishes rose from 0.88 per 10.000 in 1999 to 1.04 in 2000.
3. The Transportation Department received 2.98 complaints for every 100,000 passengers. A 20 percent increase over the 2.48 in 1999.
4. Ten carriers were on time 72.6 percent and in 1999 it was 76.1 percent for 10,000 flights.
5. Airlines mishandled or loss 529 pieces of luggage out of 1,000.

See table 3.2 for on-time arrivals and on-time departures for 1999.

Table 3.2

On Time Arrivals and Departures at US Airports 1999
(percent based on arrival and departure times of domestic flights. A flight is considered on time if it operates less than 15 minutes after schedule time. Canceled or diverted fights are late)

Airport	On Time Arrivals				On Time Departures			
	1st qtr	2d qtr	3d qtr	4th qtr	1st qtr	2d qtr	3d qtr	4th qtr
Atlanta Harsfield Intl	70.3	74.6	80.6	80.3	78.4	79.3	83.8	85.3
Baltimore/Washington Intl	78.8	76.2	82.1	83.9	85.1	80.1	85.5	85.8
Boston Logan Intl	65.9	65.2	74.8	75.4	81.3	77.2	81.4	82.4
Chicago, O'Hare	75.3	75.1	76.8	80.1	77.8	74.3	77.5	81.5
Dallas-Ft Worth Regional	82.7	84.9	84.9	81.8	82.5	83.5	82.5	80.6
Denver Intl	80.9	77.7	80.6	79.4	81.4	80.5	81.9	82.1
Detroit Metro Wayne	78.6	70.6	64.2	84.4	75.3	64.3	60.2	81.4
Las Vegas McCarran Intl	74.7	75.8	77.3	73.2	75.9	78.9	76.3	75.2
Los Angeles Intl	71.4	70.5	79.1	74.5	75.5	79.4	82.1	80.5
Miami Intl	74.7	79.7	73.8	81.3	81.2	83.8	78.5	86.1
New York Kennedy Intl	67.6	71.4	80.1	85.6	80.9	81.5	84.3	88.1
New York LaGuardia	72.9	69.8	76.2	78.3	83.1	80.1	82.8	83.7
Philadelphia Intl	71.5	71.5	77.4	78.1	77.6	75.3	78.6	77.2
St. Louis Lamer	72.2	74.3	81.1	82.5	74.6	74.2	81.6	83.6
San Diego Intl	73.2	72.1	79.3	74.1	77.6	80.6	83.1	80.4
San Francisco Intl	58.1	61.7	69.3	67.5	65.6	73.1	76.9	74.7
Seattle-Tacoma Intl	72.8	73.6	75.8	67.1	80.9	82.7	78.9	76.4

Source: U.S. Department of Consumer Affairs Air Travel Consumers Report.

Blame It On The Weather

Representative John Dingell, a Michigan Democrat, introduced a bill called Bill of Rights. Northwest Airline passengers were stranded on an airplane when a snowstorm shut down the airport in Detroit. The passengers were kept on board for over eight hours. The airline promised to do better, but promises are only promises said Dingell and Congress. The airlines must do better to protect the flying public. Senator John McCain, an Arizona Republican chairman of the Committee on Commerce Science and Transportation said, he would introduce legislation to improve customer service and that consumers have information about chronically delayed flights. He also said the minimum compensation for involuntary bumped passengers should be increased, and airlines should be clear about how passengers who are detained overnight will be treated. Flexibility among the airlines. Meaning one airline is providing different service than other's. A legislated program would be a one-size-fits-all. Not even the one size has been tried to see if it fits all.

A small portion of help in delays is temporary during the warmer months when snow and ice has left the area. But some parts of weather will still be the dictator, like gusty winds and fog. To help the stranded passengers at Massport Logan Airport, it is during what other big airports have done to make a small attempt to ease the problems. In February of 2001, Massachusetts Port Authority provided overnight lodgings in the airport even to the angry passengers that lived in Boston. The exit doors at the airport are secured to prevent people from getting in or out. If they could be opened from the inside only, that could present problems.

In Des Moines Iowa in February 2001, an airliner made an emergency landing because a passenger was sick. After the sick passenger left the airplane, it failed to take off. The crew discovered mechanical problems or did the crew just want some rest? No attention was given to the stranded passengers. The planes crew went to a hotel, the passengers were told to remain in the big quite terminal, and services were shut down for the night. The only thing they had was a lot of light from the ceiling. They tried to sleep on the hard floor or benches while hungry even though some had eaten a small bag of bagels on the airplane.

Now when ten or more people are stranded overnight because of bad weather, Massport will supply the disgruntled travelers sleeping cots, but the airlines will have to provide pillows and blankets depending on what caused the delay. Does this really mean if nine persons are stranded or if the delay does not depend on weather, they will not be able to get a cot and a pillow to try and sleep on?

Along with the 500 cots, Massport will supply food bags, diapers, formulas, coloring books, and crayon for the young or anyone that wants to use them. (food bags were used to hold feed for horses) They will be stored at each of five terminals at Logan. Also Massport will supply bottled water and food will consist of long shelf life items that does not require refrigeration as candy bars that is classified as food. Cleaning crews will spray the cots with disinfectant after each use. Will there be inspectors or supervisors that monitor the spraying? Concession stands that have a contract with Sky Chief for catering will remain open later than usual and provide food that will temporally help their hunger. If passengers are stranded after the concession stands close, they cannot get any of that food.

There are also more responsibilities for the airlines. If flights are delayed or canceled because of mechanical problems with air traffic systems, labor issues or crew problems, airline managers can decide "if or how much to assist travelers." It only sounds good, but decisions will always favor the airlines.

Safety Overlooked To Keep Planes In Air

The US News Report talked about one airline that continued to have maintenance problems. In November 3, 2000, American West Airlines left Phoenix for Orange County in California. Two boxes containing computer equipment broke lose beneath the cockpit disabling vital functions of the Airbus they were flying. The pilot was able to turn around and land, says Tom Pailey, a Federal Aviation Administration Inspector. After examination, it found that the boxes had not been secured properly.

The National Transportation Safety Board focused on another airline carrier. Alaska Airline MD-83 crashed off the California coast on January 31, 2000. Investigators believe poor maintenance played a part. The FAA knew and told the airline company of problems months before the tragedy and often routinely found cracked windows, leaking lavatories, and inoperative thrust reverses on the same airline. It was the ninth-largest airline, but in 1998 the FAA cited the airline for at least 20 alleged maintenance related violations.

American West aircraft's were found to be flying in non-airworthy conditions and a reliable Rolls-Royce engine failed or had to be shut down in flight three times. FAA was questioning the competency, qualifications, and commitment of America West. A veteran FAA inspector said, planes land at Sky Harbor International Airport in Phoenix and the maintenance mechanic said, a famous expression around here is, "don't gold-plate the airplane," meaning keep the repairs to a minimum.

The airline company was founded by Beauvais, but it declared bankruptcy in 1991. He was replaced by William France that slashed costs and the airline began a growth in this country and foreign airports. In December 1995, the company fired 500 maintenance workers and began contracting its heavy maintenance in an attempt to save money. The quality of work declined and mistakes piled up because of corporate pressure to maintain schedules. According to procedures, the manufacturer Boeing, recommended repairs to the landing gear and other critical components, but the notices were ignored. Most of the cases resulted in components malfunctioning and grounding says Ox who also heads the local unit of the Air Line.

Deadly Maintenance and Health Problems

After receiving an airplane from being overhauled, there would be many things wrong with it. One very noticable case was a disconnected pneumatic line that sent toxic hydraulic fumes into the cabins of a Boeing 737 that caused passengers to get sick. That was the results of a maintenance man not during his job correctly.

Making figures look good on paper can be easily done, but the effects of it in real life will be shown in some way. The new group of maintenance workers were not direct employees of American West and their driving force was probably during enough work for a paycheck. They had no determined interest in the airplanes. Did they have experience on the Boeing airplane? It had no major accidents, but FAA audits teams in January and July, said Phoenix inspectors were overlooking repair jobs. They claimed that slipshod maintenance threatened their record. They found laxed oversight by contractors, high management turnover, confusing procedures, and a deteriorating working relationship with FAA in some areas.

Then there was politics. Since the FAA had cited numerous findings, Phoenix wondered why agency managers had not moved more aggressively against American West. Key recommendations had been overruled by headquarters on several occasions. If a boss tell's a man working under him to react in certain ways, if the employee wants to keep his or her job, they followed their orders. This also happens if the boss of the employee wants to move up. FAA headquarters inspectors and outside auditors suggested that the FAA halt America West growth until its maintenance problems were satisfied, but management said there was no justification for that option. The airline did agree to curtail its schedule and add more employees. The maintenance workers were replaced.

While air travel was continuing to grow, FAA inspectors were being stretched so that they had to accomplished in hours what they did in days. One hundred thirty seven inspectors covered 2,210 aviation manufacturing plants (16 manufacturer's each). In 1973 the same number of inspectors were responsible for about 600 aviation manufacturing plants (that's a little over 4 manufacturing plants each). The FAA also had a Training Fund that was cut by 80 percent and classes for repairing aging aircraft and other crucial issues were routinely canceled. Jim Pratt inspects manufacturers in Michigan and said, "more airplanes will fall out of the sky."

Poor maintenance caused or contributed to at least six of 18 major aviation accidents in mid 1996 according to the National Transportation Safety Board.

Six mechanical failures and the results:

1. Federal Express Flight 1406 on September 5, 1996, Newburgh, New York, had a fire that started in the cabin cargo compartment of a DC-10 forcing an emergency landing probably caused by a flammable liquid.

2. Delta Air Lines flight 1288 on July 6, 1996, in Pensacola, Florida, a MD-88 had engine failure on takeoff cause by flying debris hitting pieces of the fuselage. Results, two dead and five injured. Metal fatigue caused cracks.
3. Fire erupted on ValuJet Airlines flight 597 on June 8, 1995, in Atlanta after shrapnel from a right engine penetrated the fuselage and a fuel line on takeoff. The takeoff was aborted, but 7 were injured and that was caused by fatigue.
4. ValuJet Airlines flight 592 on May 11, 1996, in Miami, had a fire that engulfed the cabin of a DC-9. Oxygen generators were improperly placed in the cargo hole and ignited as a result of a maintenance worker not securing them. The airplane crashed in the Everglades killing all 110 aboard.
5. MD-68 Trans World Airlines flight 800 on July 6, 1996, in Pensacola, Florida, a fuel tank on a Boeing 747 exploded over the Atlantic Ocean shortly after takeoff. Aged electrical wiring was suspected of generating a spark. All 230 aboard died.
6. Atlantic Southeast Airlines flight 529 on August 21, 1995, in Georgia, a blade on the left propeller of Embraer-120 separated causing loss of lift and control. The plane crashed killing 8 and injuring 21. A fatigue crack was discovered in the propeller.

Fatigue is an overworked part that needs to be replaced.

Flight 587 took off from the John F. Kennedy International Airport in November and crashed in Queens, NY shortly after lift-off killing all aboard. Data showed the captain made a remark about a wake encounter that could have been caused by a large Boeing 747-400 that took off immediately before flight 587. American Airline, flight 587, took off two minutes and twenty seconds after the Boeing 747-400. It began moving down the runway only ninety seconds after a Japan airlines jumbo jet started its takeoff roll.

The American Airline plane crossed the departure route of the Japan jumbo jet almost immediately after liftoff and radar data showed it then followed a path that was parallel to the Japan jumbo jet's path. Authorities also said the American flight closed to within 90 seconds of the Japan jet at the time it began to fall apart and spiral to the ground.

There are minitorandos at the ends of both wings which is a whirling motion of air that tends to form a cavity or vacuum in the center of the circle and draw toward the vacuum. The pressure of the exhaust from both airplanes must have added to the turbulence. With the number of larger airplanes increasing at airports, will this be a growing problem?

Passengers losing lives and getting injured because of problems that should not happen should be red flags for better maintenance, but there are many pressures put on the right authorities to keep the airplanes in the skies.

O'Hare and LaGuardia Airports

O'Hare and Midway both have been expanded and modernized in recent years, but O'Hare Airport is the center of the airline industry and the city presses for still more expansion. Citizens' groups focused on areas south of Chicago where many opposed locating a new super-airport. Agreeing are elected officials in Du Page and Northwest Cook County who are sick of O'Hare's noise, safety problems, and overcrowding. They campaigned fiercely against plans to add runways at O'Hare and demanded a third airport be put elsewhere. The expansion could result in more than one million flights a year taking off or landing there, up from 800,000.

Butler is chairman of a coalition that previously relocated 300,000 residents for O'Hare. He pointed out that there were 191,000 people living in nearby communities before the first jet flew. Some now sit with their wives and cannot hear one another talk as the dishes rattled.

There is a fear of loss of jobs, added fees, and political strength if a new airport is built somewhere else. When competitors started pushing hard for outlying sites, Chicago Mayor Richard Daley called for a new $5 billion airport on land formerly occupied by a steel mill on the southeast side of the city. The city would demolish 8,500 homes where people live obliterating the Hegewisch neighborhood, move 47 businesses that employ 9,000 workers, and reroute the Calumet River. You do not need to be a genius to foresee the new problems this huge airport would create and the money that would be spent.

Noise problems are so bad that 13 municipalities filed a class-action lawsuit against O'Hare on grounds of emotional and physical damage, and they are committed to carrying it to the United States Supreme Court. Congressman Henry Hide of Illinois has advised school districts to sue the City of Chicago because sound-proofing funds have never been provided to area schools.

There are other problems than noisy jets. The airplanes with new designed engines are quieter, but emit more nitrogen oxide. We complain about what we can see and hear, but do not realized some of the things in the air that affects our health cannot be seen or heard. Would you rather be hard of hearing and breath fresher air or have better hearing while breathing in more polluted air? When we think of pollution we generally think of vehicles, buses, and big trucks, but seldom think about all of the pollution jets emit at busy airports. When we see the well designed airplanes taking off and landing, we pay a price for the convenience of flying. There are comments that extra runways will eliminate some emissions because airplanes will not be idling as long on runways. Its the taking off of the planes that really emit nitrogen oxide.

If a new airport is built, it should be a noticable distance from Chicago and other surrounding cities. Designed with the airport would be train links to inner-cities with stations along the links. Incoming passengers and their baggage from an airline would automatically be transferred to a train alleviating the traffic problems in the parking lots and gridlocks to the cities. One train replaces 300 vehicles. This would decrease trip time and increase the enjoyment of the trip for the passenger.

Airline Lottery

The FAA held a lottery to "reduce" the number of flights using LaGuardia, which accounts for almost one quarter of all United State delays. In 1999, a lottery was designed to reduce air traffic by 20 percent, but did not become effective until 2001. It was called a stop gap until the FAA could come up with a solution to the problems created by a law designed to provide service to cities that are about 300 miles away using smaller airplanes.

Parts of the lottery was for daily round trips to New York from Hanscom Field in Bedford, Massachusetts. The airplanes would take off from another airport, but land at overcrowded LaGuardia. There were already to many airplanes, so how could adding more airplanes for short trips create more runway space? The airplanes are smaller, but still need runways. Too many airlines signed up for lottery slots.

LaGuardia is a small older airfield with only two runways and the facility is 680 acres. John F. Kennedy International Airport 10 miles away covers 4,930 acres, but LaGuardia handles 33 percent more flights daily.

Connecticut based Shuttle America was one of the new airlines that applied for seven daily flights to LaGuardia from Hanscom field. The federal Department of Transportation approved the request, but delayed it for six weeks. Connecticut base shuttle received seven slots which is just what they wanted saying there was a "hole" in the evening, between 6 p.m. to 9 p.m. The Legend Airlines, Texas based, was given 7 slots even without their aircraft's operating. Later the Connecticut shuttle ceased their operations.

What compounded the existing problems? The Federal Aviation Administration permitted 159 take offs and landings at already overcrowded New York's LaGuardia Airport. Airplanes for short flights are smaller and are not loaded at the regular loading ramps if there are any at that airport. If it is raining or snowing, passengers board a waiting bus on the tarmac with their luggage that carry them to the smaller airplane. Leaving the bus they stand in line again with their luggage to board the airplane.

LaGuardia airport had the most delays in the nation. The FAA said in 1999 the nation had 374,116 delays out of 165,851,516 and in 2000, there were 450,289 delays out of 166,526,769 flights. That figures to be 67,525 more flights in one year or an increase of 40% with more people landing at LaGaurdia.

The airport had 9,226 planes late taking off or landing during October in 1999 only. One day, 600 aircraft could not arrive or depart on time. This is a good way to hold passengers hostages and not be punished by law. The FAA has labeled the situation intolerable, but what are they going to do about it? How could they not have seen the approaching problem and tried to solve it? It is much easier to look at the present situations and complain. We have high paid planners and engineers that have computers to play with figures, however there is still politics that play a big part in how much money will be spent, how it will be spend, and when.

A report for 2000 said, LaGuardia had a 15 percent increase in the number of flights compared to the same month in 1999. Delays based on volume had increased 14 times that accounted for 24.2 percent of total delays and 39.2 percent of all volume delays. In October the airport's delays accounted for 23 percent of the US total and 57 percent of all volume delays.

At a few airports, flight controllers can handle about 7 aircraft operating every five minutes without compromising safety. That's one airplane every 43 seconds or 3/4 of a minute. Now 22 planes are trying to be squeezed into that time slot which is one airplane every 14 seconds or 1/4 of a minute. At O'Hare airfield years ago, I counted 35 airplanes lined one behind each other and each took flight every minute. Fourteen seconds does not seem real unless more than one runway is used at the same time.

Airplane Freighters

Since airplane freighters take off and land at the same airports as passenger airplanes and they both carry cargo, I will give information on them with comments on their growth. Steel-wheel and maglev trains also carry cargo.

A magazine article titled, "Expansion Seen For Air Cargo Industry," said there were more than 1,623 jet air freighters in operation worldwide in 2000. The size of the fleet doubled in the past 10 years just trying to meet an ever-growing demand for global air cargo services. Passengers out number freight by more than a seven to one ratio, but cargo traffic has grown faster than passenger traffic during the past decade worldwide. Air cargo increased from approximately 54.8 billion ton miles in 1990 to an estimated 102.8 billion ton miles in 2000. The annual growth increased about 6.5 percent which is about 2 percentage points higher than the annual growth for passenger traffic during that period. Airline trade organizations in Europe and the United States reported an 8-10 percent growth in cargo traffic. Carriers have reported record cargo growth based on full economic recovery in some regions.

Freight traffic is intended to grow at an average annual rate of about 6 percent during the next twenty years from 1999, and passenger growth will not be much above 5 percent. Freight manufacturers are growing in response to an every expanding volume of global trade. Air freight is more expensive than other transportation, but it is ideally suited to meet the needs of shippers as they demand faster and more reliable deliveries given increasingly more complex supply gains. Goods that are considered as high-value are particularly suited for transport by air based on values and air freight items represent an estimated 40 percent of all goods moving globally.

There will be expanding demands for freight aircraft. At present in the year of 2000, the world's fleet of freighters have individual payloads from 25,000 lbs to more than 240,000 lb capacity, 120 tones. Fewer than 25 percent of those aircraft's were delivered from the factory in an all-cargo configuration. The remaining 75 percent operated for 15 to 20 years carrying passengers. Then they were converted to freighter configurations which is an exceptional way to extend the useful economic lives of commercial aircraft that otherwise would have ended their service.

Airbus and Boeing offer factory-built freighter versions of existing passenger models, and each has new freighters being designed. The two industries see a way to increase their financial intake. Major airframe companies are now leading the way in developing freighter conversion programs for newer airplane types. Boeing and Airbus know that there is money to be made in the modification market and they understand the existence of a follow-on market for used aircraft that can stimulate aircraft sales. Since Boeing originally designed the airplane, they have documentation and analysis related to the unmodified aircraft. It also means they can more readily satisfy the FAA and other regulatory bodies. Any proposed modification will not adversely impact airworthiness or increase modification time.

Boeing is teaming up with outside parties such as Israel Aircraft Industries, Aeronavali, and Singapore Technologies creating joint ventures for freighter conversion giving such companies a continued role. Global air cargo traffic will approach 342.5 billion ton miles by 2020, compared with 102.8 billion tone miles in 2000. The manufacturers know there will be a continued markets for new and converted freighters. It is estimated freighter fleets will double while the traffic levels more than triple creating a robust financial future for crowding the airports. About 1,000 airplanes will be withdrawn from service resulting in the need for more than 3,100 freighters to be added over a 20-year period for growing and replacement purposes.

New Designs

Many of the freighters added to the world wide fleet in the 1980-1995 period were small-capacity airplanes that carried payloads of 40,000 to 60,000 lbs for the express companies like FedEx and UPS. Now the fast growing freighter market has been in the medium-capacity wide-body category. These planes carry payloads between 80,000-120,000 lbs and larger freighters will be available in the future.

Most people do not realized that a large portion of cargo is handled by the world's airlines and moves freight in carrying compartment of passenger airplanes. The wide-body passenger airplanes provide competition to freighters. They have space for 5 or 6 pallets of freight in addition to the space used for passenger baggage.

Air Bus is working on a model that will have a stretched fuselage and has space for 36 main deck pallets. It will have three decks, but Boeing states it will be difficult to load. Why would a manufacturing company put that much money in something that may not sell? The companies that believe in the manufacture of the Airbus airplanes are Emirate that has an order for two, Atlas Airm Singapore Airlines, FedEx, Lufthansa, and Cargolus have shown considerable interest. The purchase price will be unbelievable.

How will the US handle all of the new and old passenger airplanes and new and old freighters? It is a necessity that steel-wheel trains or maglev trains be used to help the growing problems that can also carry freight. Texas, Midwest, and Arizona has a lot of flat areas for trains to use.

McDonnell Douglas, Boeing, and Airbus industries of Europe are racing to meet the buying frenzy for new passenger airplanes. As of early 1990, Boeing's combined order books were crammed with more than $160 billion worth of aircraft, with delivery dates stretched beyond the 21st century. Domestic airlines alone had a record 2,000 new aircraft on order. Boeing production of 737s rose from 14 per month in the late 1980s to 21 per month in 1991 about one aircraft per work day.

Airbus will quadruple its output from 45 aircraft annually to more than 299 aircraft. Larger sections of their airplanes can be fitted together by attaching different section rather than building new airplanes. A portion of those will be needed to replace aging aircraft which brings up the key point, 7,000 aircraft will be added to the system world-wide to meet travel growth. The majority of the new aircraft will be the short-distance jetliners that are to be the life blood of the manufacturers creating new problems at airports that Supertrains should be making. Boeing estimated that the greatest number of units sold will be the Boeing 737, McDonnell Douglas MD-80 series, and Airbus A-320 aircraft. They are all short-range.

Help From The Government

Generous subsidies exist for aircraft research and development. The biggest beneficiary is the world's biggest maker of commercial jetliners, Boeing. Working around the clock, it manufactures more aircraft than McDonnell Douglas and Air Bus combined. The workhorse for many airlines are the companies narrow-body 727s, 737s, 757s, and the wide body 767s.

Boeing is building the largest structural parts ever made from composite materials for aircraft advancing their production and designs. Technology made some very important advances on fighter airplanes that is used for commercial aircraft, Dale G. Shoehorn Boeings B-3 project manager told Aviation Week. Some of those advances came from designs of fighter planes paid for by the government. How much of the Boeing 777 was paid by the Government?

The Essential Air Services program is one of the better pieces of pork-barrel legislation in Washington and despite the deficit problem, few in Congress are likely to vote it out of business said Kathryn B. Creedy, owner of Global Airline Enterprises. Texas is the only state without any type of aviation fuels tax, and still does not spend anything for new rail passenger service.

The recent terrorist attack of September 2001 caused different outlooks and reactions in the number of airplanes being manufactured and the number expected to be sold. The passengers load factors dropped well under 50 percent after their return to service. Major

United States carriers cut airline capacity by 20 percent, instituted layoffs, and used smaller aircraft based on the low load factors. They will downsize aircraft, ground many of the older aircraft, and delay new deliveries. United Airlines planned to reduce about 1,900 daily flights from a worldwide schedule. This was a month before winter and two months before Christmas.

Chapter 4: America is Growing

Problems and Growth

America is growing and that means more airplanes, vehicles, more pollution, more lost hours in congestion, and more accidents and deaths indicated by the statistics from the Census Bureau said Director Kenneth Parewitt. Explanations on growth is provided so the reader can have a background on how the population has grown and the additional problems created and will continued to be created. America will continue to grow faster emphasizing the importance of traveling by trains and reducing traveling time.

Most immigrants came from Europe at the start of the century, and very few came from Latin America that reversed by century's end. Two million immigrants came from Italy and only 50,000 from Mexico between 1901 and 1979. At one point eight million more came from Mexico and 54,000 from Italy.

During the next ten years, the world-population is expected to grow by 959 million, the largest increment ever for a single decade according to Lester R. Brown in the World Watch Institute's State of The World. That many people includes the United Kingdom, Belgium, Denmark, Ireland, Norway, and Sweden. All of the people in the United States will need more energy for heating and transportation that accounts for nearly two-thirds of all oil used in the world.

In 1955, 29 percent of married women were in the labor force, but in 1998 that figure jumped to 61 percent. In 1900, only 3 million Americans were 65 or older, compared with 34 million in 1997. Sixty percent of Americans lived in rural areas in 1900, but Florida had 530,000 residents in 1900 compared with 14.9 million in the most recent census in 2001. The average household had 4.8 people in 1900, and by 1998, it was only 2.6.

American women in 1900 could expect to live to age 48, two years more than the life expectancy for American men. By 1997 life expectancy for women was 79 and men 74. There were 36 highway traffic fatalities in 1900 compared with 81.7 million in 1999 and America has been first since the 1900s in the beginning of the century.

Texas population has grown the most and it also had the highest temperatures during the summer and the smoggiest days. It is flat land where trains could easily be used for the public while reducing smog. The population will continued to grow as more companies relocate there.

The populations size in 1990, gain by 2000, and percent of change are listed in table 4.1. Highway and gasoline lobbyist and Detroit with their large sums of money stands in the way of rail travel.

Table 4.1

Ten States Population Growth and Gain

States	1990 Population	Gain Year 2000	Percent Change
Idaho	1,293,953	287,204	22
Nevada	1,998,257	796,424	40
Utah	2,233,169	510,319	23
Colorado	4,301,261	1,006,867	23
Arizona	5,130,632	1,465,404	28
Washington	5,894,121	1,027,429	17
N. Carolina	8,049,313	1,420,676	18
Georgia	8,186,453	1,708,237	21
Florida	15,982,378	3,044,452	19
Texas	20,851,620	3,865,310	18

Source: U.S. Census Bureau Director Kenneth Prewitt.

Oil Thirsty Vehicles Sold Annually

See table 4.2 for the vehicles sold from 1992 to 1997. In 1988, a Time Magazine had an article that said the average motorist will spend an estimated six months of his lifetime waiting for "red lights" to change according to a study by Priority Management in Pittsburgh, a time-management consulting firm.

Table 4.2

Motor Vehicles Sold Per Model Year 1992 to 1997
(8,160 represents 8,160,000 per model year beginning Oct. 1 and ending Sept 30)

Item	1992	1993	1994	1995	1996	1997
New Car Sales	8,160	8,428	8,936	8,736	8,654	8,250
New Truck Sales	4,707	5,486	6,244	6,498	6,806	7,121
Total Sales	12,867	13,914	15,180	15,234	15,460	15,371

Source: U.S. Breau of Economic Analysis

America's insatiable appetite for petroleum is unbelievable. The United States has only two percent of the world's population, but consumes a quarter of the world's oil. This nation, which uses more oil than any other country, spent a large $1.1 trillion of its wealth on oil imports between 1970 and 1989. The big overpowered vehicles and fuel-thirsty jetliners leaves America open to the threat of fuel shortages that would devastate the economy. This country remains painfully vulnerable to disruptions in supplies from the Middle East where undependable or even hostile powers control oil wells.

The United States needs to lessen oil use. Compared to the rest of the world, the nation's petroleum reserves are small. Failure to reduce oil dependency only places the nation at the mercy of oil-rich countries. There have been about 15 oil supply shortages. Twice in the 1970s the United States suffered an energy crisis that sent shock waves. In the 1970s there were long lines of vehicles at the remaining service stations when gasoline was difficult to buy because of projected shortages.

More use of the steel-wheel and maglev train that should be in operation this year in 2002, and as more and more people increase the ridership there will be a decrease in the use of oil.

Chapter 5: Worldwide Warming

Greenhouse Effect

Worldwide warming is included because it is caused by burning of forest fires and pollution from vehicles and airplanes that keeps growing with no end. It is increasing and is caused by humans as more toxin enters the atmosphere. Research indicates one effect of global warming is caused by burning fossil fuels. There are pollutants that harms the health of many people, but they do not realize it. If all toxicants stopped being released in the atmosphere, it would remain there for decades. With the populations and the number of vehicles growing, the most America can do is slow the increasing ozone levels. Riding trains will not solve the worldwide warming, but no single action will. Riding trains will help in the heavily populated urban areas where more people will have their lungs damaged.

What is this global warming and the greenhouse effect? The greenhouse warming effects results directly from the sun that is very hot and earth that is relatively cool. It starts when our sun floods earth with a bath of warm energy. The atmosphere, acting like an insulating blanket or the glass in a greenhouse, keeps some of that heat from escaping back into space. The results is a temperature regulation system that keep things just right for life, not to hot and not too cold. Human activity has increased the proportion of certain atmosphere components called greenhouse gases and the result is a rise in global temperatures held near the earth by the atmosphere.

The gas that has been a chief malefactor in the greenhouse story is carbon dioxide. The rise in carbon dioxide is due in part to the increased combustion of fossil fuels. It is the single largest waste product of modern society. That added to more than five billion tons of carbon from fossil fuels in 1988.

Green plants are a principal consumer or a sink for carbon dioxide. That is why burning tropical forest for agriculture, cattle, and cooking fuel contribute. The Brazilian fires in the northeast, and in the southeast in the United States put significant amounts of carbon dioxide into the air.

Burning tropical forests to provide room for more cattle ranches, changes from one to a triple effort. Large fell forest trees make a wonderful home for termites and the end results is the same as cows, methane.

Methane is the second most important greenhouse gas we are adding to the atmosphere after carbon dioxide. One of the sources is emissions from solid waste dumps, coal mining, and natural gas leaks. Large amounts of methane originate in a surprising place, the digestive tract of cows. Between 3 and 10 percent of cattle fodder, cattle food, is turned into methane. It has been estimated that there are 1.2 billion head of cattle on earth and all of them belch furiously. The average cow belches up to 400 liters of methane a day, and the yearly global contribution is about 1 million tons from cows alone. The cattle farms produce 1.4 billion tones of animal waste which contaminate drinking water, kill fish, and spread disease. Cattle dun also emits methane.

Global warming is increased by smog generated on earth and evidence suggests that rising carbon dioxide levels in the atmosphere could continue to trigger warming of the earth's climate with potentially devastating consequences. Environmentalists and Evironmental Protection Agency officials warn that without a threatened crackdown on "highway use and construction vehicles," it will continue.

I mentioned these things to give and idea where other world warming comes from harming our health. Since riding trains will not eliminate the problems, it can help in the urban areas that are heavily populated keeping the ozone level down making it better for our health. There are some that are skeptical about this being a worldwide problems. All they need to do is remember when the nuclear plant in Russia exploded emitting radiation. About a week or two later, a large dark cloud passed over the east coast carrying the radiated pollution. The first of the year in 2001, dust clouds formed over the Arabian and African deserts and it rose high enough to travel to the United States that was seen in the air.

Icebergs Melting

Scientist have discovered and iceberg they named Godzilla. It was the largest iceberg ever seen by human eyes. This crashing behemoth, whose slow speed and size could have endangered shipping lanes that carry supplies to McMurdo research base in Antarctic. It was a dangerous dynamic iceberg that had broken off a larger block of ice and shedded huge pieces of ice since its birth during the month of March in the year of 2000. In the year of 2001, it was less than half its original size which was about twice the surface area of Rhode Island, and nearly as long as the state of Massachusetts. As it continued through the turbulent sea, it shedded huge slabs of ice as it groaned, crackled, and heaved.

In the ocean, the action is at the edges for biologists, explained Gregory Stone, the New England Aquarium's Conservation Director and Co-Leader of the expedition. Godzilla is the most prominent among any of a number of new icebergs this year by seawater that has become warmer in the Southern Ocean, a change that most scientists attribute to global warming. Many of the icebergs are off a larger piece of ice from the Antarctic ice shelf that extends from the frozen continent.

Indians in Iceland has said the winter's are not as cold and the permafrost is not as deep as it has been. The weather starts getting warmer sooner than what they call normal based on past years with the continued result of global warming. The oceans will continue to get warmer, more and more giant icebergs will be seen, and this could be problems for the shipping lanes. A few years in the past, another large iceberg was floating in the sea moving in the direction of shipping lanes, but we did not here anymore about it.

Approximately 10,000 icebergs float in the ocean each year with the tallest seen equal to a 50 story building with only 10 percent visible above water. They usually travel up to 27 miles per day and melts at a rate of 10 feet per day.

There are other areas the result of warming that is also harmful to our health that most people are not even aware of. Worldwide warming is blamed on the decline of coral reef in many parts of the world. Bleaching occurs when coral is diseased or under stress and expels the symbiotic that it normally harbors. The calcium carbonate skeleton then shows through, giving a pale or stark white appearance to the coral.

Health Risk Worldwide

Many people will be surprised by the relatively high level of health risk associated with air toxins in their area said Bill Pease, a toxicologist at the New York based Environmental Defense Fund who obtained the EPA results. There are a lot of things we do every day, but do not realize it has a toxic consequences as dry clothe cleaners and businesses. There are 148 chemicals such as formaldehyde, carbon, tetrachloride, phthalate, benzene, chloroform, ethylene, dichloride, and methyl chloride in the air.

Most of these chemicals are not recognized by us, but Americans increase their risk of cancer practically every time they draw breath outdoors. A place to escape toxic chemicals in the air "does not exist." The Environmental Protection Agency found that every American inhales unsafe levels of at least eight chemical, and 20 million Americans face at least a 10,000 life time risk of getting cancer a result of a 1990 Cumulative Exposure Project.

Another producer of pollution is airplanes at busy airports all over this world. Jets emit tons of oxides every year that is an ingredient in acid rain that harms trees and wildlife. Logan airport ranks sixth on the list of the worst emitters of smog and Robert Duand predicts Logan airport will rank number one by 2010. The new jets are quieter, but their redesigned engines release more nitrogen oxide that has been mentioned earlier. We usual think of pollution coming from cars and trucks, but jet airplanes emit tons of nitrogen oxides every year. Logan Airport and all of the bigger airports also cause vibration, other air pollution, and noise.

The year of 2000 went down in history as being among the warmest of the past 106 years as well as one of the ten wettest on record. United States National Oceanic and Atmospheric Administration found that the average annual United States temperature for 2000 was about 54.2 degrees Fahrenheit at year's end. The temperatures were well over the average of 52.8 degrees and could indicate that this has been one of the ten hottest years in our history. It is believed this is because of our pollution and the greenhouse gases. The increase in airplanes, vehicles, buses, and the large increase in population is contributing to the warming of the world.

Texas will have to stop the urban sprawl that increases smog by inducing people not to drive their vehicles as much. The Texas Department of Transportation forecasts another 45 percent increase in driving statewide by 2017, on top of a 325 percent increase since 1967. It will not be able to stop the urban areas from growing as more people move there and more houses are built, but it is necessary that a commuter-rail train be used for less pollution and more conveniences. Riders on one train remove 300 vehicles from the road.

Most of the worlds energy comes from oil, coal, and natural gas that emit some 22 billion tons of carbon dioxide into the Earth's Atmosphere each year. Such emission could rise 55 percent by 2020 as populations swell, according to the US Department of Energy.

Coal is the filthiest fuel gouged from the ground and has more carbon than any other fuel. When burned, it releases carbon, mercury, lead, and sulfur into the air. China and India are projected to account for the greatest rise in the use of coal. With only 7 percent of the world's population, North America consumes 30 percent of the world's energy. Such gluttony could shift as developing nations, mainly in Asia and South America, demand more constantly increasing pollution.

It is imperative to accept the idea that we are connected to all things in this world and when there is a change in one area we all are effected. The world is warming and the oceans will rise. It is difficult to realize, but only a little imagination is needed when you see the beeches of some cities. All of the big hotels in Miami are built a few feet from the edge of the ocean with an assurance there will never be any danger. The beaches at the Cape at Martha's Vineyard are being continually washed away. The hotels in Atlanta and New Jersey has stores and gambling casinos with basements built on the edges of the beaches. There was a storm in New Jersey with high winds near the gambling casinos that caused major damages as water stood in the buildings and basements.

Worldwide Changes

The Atlantic Ocean widens up to 1.5 inches a year and the Red Sea widens 0.8 of an inch in a year. This is not much, but consider if increasing numbers of icebergs keep breaking loose and more snow on mountains keep melting, there will be a difference as they melt and increase the amount of water. This is another reason we should stop increasing the growing of pollution by riding trains.

A report from researchers in 99 nations that met in China said, increased floods, killer storms, and droughts are caused by global warming. The global temperatures could rise 10.5 degrees Fahrenheit in the next century causing more bad weather and flooding. Since the 1980s, temperatures have kept rising. In November of 2000, there were talks on how best to cut emissions from power plants, factories, and vehicles that causes heat in the atmosphere. If emissions are lowered, oil use has to be decreased.

A few years back, the undeveloped countries were asked to stop their pollution as well as the United States. Some of the comments were, the United States has already developed their country, yet they want countries like China to reduce their emission when they are building up their country and would emit more. Emissions per person increased 3.4 percent between 1990 and 1997 and the number of persons also increased causing a double edge.

Barrette Rock, coordinator for the federally mandated New England Regional Assessment said, we could have less colorful foliage and continued coastal storms. The manager for Maple Grove Farms of Vermont that makes candy and syrup said, maple syrup from the trees has started sugaring earlier. Texas had record setting days of 100-degree F, and glaciers in the north have started melting. Most climate watchers agree that the temperature increase worldwide in the last century is partly caused by human actions burning oil and other fossil fuels. When we burn gasoline in cars, wood for heat, and forests burn because of lightning, the gasses are trapped in the Earth's atmosphere and re-radiated toward earth making a warmer blanket.

One hundred scientists meeting in Shanghai said, new evidence shows the 21st century temperature increases could be even more dramatic than the 1.8 to 6.3 degrees Fahrenheit predicted by the Inter-Governmental Panel on Climate Change. The Panel said that a more modest temperature jump could increase temperatures and the worldwide sea levels could climb to 17 inches. If that happens, all low-lying areas could be under water including parts of Nantucket. As we hear the figures and what is perceived as causes, we must realize that it will happen, it is just a matter of when.

Rising Sea Levels

The hotels that line Miami's beach could stand waterlogged, abandoned, and malaria could be a public health threat in Vermont. Rising sea levels could contaminate the aquifers that supply drinking water for Caribbean Islands, while entire pacific islands could simply disappear in the sea. In Bangladesh thousands of people already are dying from floods each year. Increased snow melting in the Himalayas could combine with rising seas to make at least 10 percent of the country uninhabitable.

Peter Gleick, president of the Pacific Institute for Studies in Development, Environment, and Security in Oakland, California says, no matter what we do to reduce green house-gas emissions, we will not be able to avoid some impacts of climate change. The newest global-warming forecast is backed by data from myriad satellites, weather balloons, ships at seas, and weather stations. Large commuter models of the global climate system also gives positive data.

Weather will become more unpredictable and violent with thunderstorms, increased tornadoes, and lightning sparking fires. The effects of El Nino, the atmospheric oscillation that causes flooding and mudslides in California and the tropics, would become more severe.

In the 1990s, the tab was $608 billion more than the four previous decades combined, according to World Watch Institute. Sea levels worldwide rose 9 inches in the last century, and 45 million people live at risk of flooding due to ocean surges. That figure should double if oceans rise 20 inches and it is predicted that seas will rise anywhere from 3.5 inches to 34.6 inches by 2010 largely because of thermal expansion or warmer water and because of melting glaciers and ice caps. A foot rise at the top range of the forecast would swamp parts of major cities and islands, including the Marshall Islands in the South Pacific and the Florida Keys. By 2015, it is predicted 3 billion people will be living in areas without enough water. Water-starved Middle East could become the center of conflicts and war over water.

The tropical island paradise and glistering Alpine skiing retreats may be lost in future generations, while melting ice caps in polar regions could unleash climate changes that could continue for centuries, according to a UN report released in 2001. The melting of Equatorial Glaciers in Africa and Peru is another powerful indication of global warming. Ice tops on Africa's Mount Kilimanjaro, and others in Peru and Tibet, may be disappearing the victim of a process of shrinking mountains glaciers everywhere.

Climate change could lead to:

1. Monsoons caused by denotation of our forests.
2. Heavy rains from Tropical Storms.
3. Tornadoes.
4. A complete lost of species when their habitat is lost.
5. A large lost of life.
6. Heavy floods.
7. Washed out roads and communities.
8. Droughts, Uruguay, Paraguay, Spain, Buenos, Aires, and the United States.
9. Lost of expensive property on coasts like Massachusetts, California, Florida and the Gulf of Mexico.
10. Forest fires.
11. Lost of life in Africa, Portugal, Italy, Yugoslavia, Greece, Southern Zimbabwe, Scandinavian countries, West Germany, parts of Poland, Scotland, Ireland, and England.
12. The worst displacement of populations on a large scale.
13. More changeable weather.
14. Lost of farm land and drinking water.
15. High risk from diseases carried by large numbers of mosquitoes.

Shortage of Drinking Water

I emphasize the importance of drinking water and what is estimated for the future as the vehicles and airplanes continue to contribute to pollution. We have what we think is an unlimited water resource. It evaporates from the oceans, falls to the land, and eventfully goes back to the sea. Most of the fresh water is frozen in polar ice and snow. Only 2.5 percent is fresh water, and of that fresh water only 0.6 percent is usable. Rising sea levels could turn coastal fresh water that could redistribute where and when water is available. The quality and quantity of water is deteriorating while the human population continues to grow.

As many as 80 countries already report shortages and more than a billion people do not have suitable drinking water. More than 25,000 die every day from water related disease. One of the contributors is worldwide warming that increases the evaporation, pollution, and droughts due to changes in the weather.

Another problem we have with water is acid rain that is a result of pollution from manufacturer using fossil fuel and manufacturers that burns coal. By 2010, power plants are required to reduce their sulfur dioxide emissions to 50 percent of what the 1980 level was. When you look at that statement, you realize we will never stop the emissions. The best we can hope to do is reduce emissions over a longer period of time, but it will never be enough.

Acid rain is caused when rains falls through the atmosphere. It effects our forests, many things that lives there, kills our trees, and corrodes our car's paint. About 60 percent of the sulfur dioxide comes from power plants that rely on burning fossil fuels such as coal to generate electricity. This problem is apparent more in the Northeast because the region is downwind from Midwest power plants that release high levels of sulfur dioxide.

They also produce nitrogen oxides that is a contributor to acid rain and motor vehicles also emit high levels. That acid rain falls in streams, rivers, and lakes making them more acidic. Thus making some rivers too acidic for fish. At high elevations the thin soil becomes acidic from the pollutants and dissolves nutrients that trees need to thrive on. The study's authors of the articles estimated 25 percent of the red spruces in the White Mountains have been wiped out because of acid rain, and forest and trees have not recovered because more acid is being put into the air every day. The trees once had some help as mineral buffers in the soil from calcium helped neutralize the acid, but has been depleted, thus the trees have no help. The trees do not get much calcium so they are susceptible to insects infestation and weather change says Charles T. Driscoll.

Among the countries along a river, there will be competition when the quantity of water is less and there could be fighting just to get drinking water. Every person needs a least 13 gallons of clean water a day for drinking, cooking, and sanitation says Peter Gleick. Yet a sixth of the world's people must make do with less than that. Dense population and unchecked pollution create scarcities even in Africa and Asia's wet regions. The biggest single use of water, "irrigation," cannot be recycled.

Thirty percent of all irrigation water is groundwater pumped from the High Plains aquifer that is now down so low that it would take thousands of years to recharge naturally. About 17 percent of the world's cropland is irrigated producing 40 percent of all food grown using large sums of water.

Water used for sanitation, cooking, drinking in homes, and public building is decreasing in some countries. Trying to help the situation, in 1990 most United States toilets used six gallons per flush. After 1994, 1.6 gallons were used per flush and top loading washing machines use thirty nine percent less water. However, in Africa and Asia pollution overwhelms input from rain. In many countries, less than half the population can get safe water to drink and cook with.

Needy and Hungry

From Asia to Africa, severe and long-term drought now effects more than 20 countries. In August 2000, 100 million people were suffering from drought in Africa, Central Asia, parts of the Caribbean, and Central America. Floods then wretched havoc in Cambodia, Laos, and Bangladesh. Now Mozambique is awash in floods, and a series of earthquakes has hit El Salvador. Mozambique's government in 2001 appealed for $30 million in aid.

In more tranquil Kenya, some 4.4 million people are estimated to be in urgent need of food assistance. In Nairobi, they graze their cattle in the parks of the capital city, so desperate to find grass for the cattle to eat. It is Africa and the troubled countries in the Horn of Africa where the long-term drought has had its most damaging impact, with some 16 million people facing food shortages according to UN statistics. Last year, a famine was only narrowly averted after a UN appeal.

Three years of inadequate rainfall in countries already reeling from poverty and civil unrest have reduced millions to desperate measures. In Afghanistan, tens of thousands of refugees have fled their homes in search of water and have eaten next year's seeds for food. In Tajikistan where 85 percent of the population lives below the poverty line, many of the men among the 1 million affected by drought are now migrating to Russia in hopes of finding food for their families. In war torn Angola, cattle have been dropping dead at the rate of 100 a day. In Ethiopia, the bleached bones of dead cattle liter the ground. Sudan is torn by fighting, families are selling their precious livestock which is the equivalent of American's emptying their bank accounts for a handful to eat.

Because many of those countries are pastoral societies in which people rely on their livestock as their source of food, years without rain have had a particularly devastating impact. Camels, goats, and cattle have died or being sold off. The duration of drought for nearly three years with only intermittent rainfall has produced a surge in mortality, malnutrition, and infectious disease, said Dr. Peter Salaam of the United States Centers for Disease Control in Atlanta. With people's immune systems weakened by hunger, infectious diseases like malaria and measles can rip through a population killing thousands.

In June 2001, hundreds of cholera cases were reported in drought areas. The disease also has been reported in parts of Ethiopia, where an estimated 6.2 million are affected by droughts. The World Health Organization has reported soaring rates of tuberculosis because of drought. In Sudan, where there is an 18 year old war between Islamic government to the North, Christians and rebels in the South stopped the UN from carrying in food and aid in 1998. That probably produced 100,000 deaths in the South said Robert Winter, executive director of the United States Committee for Refugees in Washington, DC.

Combined with poverty and civil unrest, it is why a near-record 60 million people worldwide now desperately need emergency assistance including food and disaster relief specialists say. Drought and other natural disasters such as earthquakes and floods are now the leading causes of food emergencies, and the number of people affected has soared from 4 million to 49 million since 1995 says the United Nations World Food Program. In the last four years, the numbers who are hungry, owing to drought, has more than quadrupled. Catherine Berating, director of Rome-Based World Food Program said, there are so many countries affected.

Meteorologists say the droughts, alone with severe flooding in other parts of the world, may stem in part from erratic weather pattern by the La Nina phase or El-Nino, with a significant shift in the temperature of the Pacific Ocean off South America. Scientist in 2001, predicted that global warming could lead to growing numbers of similar natural disasters that would have their most direct effects on the world's poorest countries.

Harvard University professor James McCarthy, chairman of the International Panel on Climate Change said, we see clear indications that there will be more extreme events. The countries that will experience the most devastating effects of this are the least equipped to handle it.

People are not just hungry, they are without any future means of livelihood. That makes it important to provide drought stricken areas with medicine and food for livestock. Tufts University Lautze said, he was very worried about the long-term future of these societies, and the world community is getting very tired of "responding."

Chapter 6: Amtrak-The Old and The New

The Old Amtrak Lost Money

In the beginning, Amtrak was recorded as one of the worst business ventures in history. It did not own any railroad stations or tracks, did not have any railroad yards or repair shops, no passenger cars or locomotives, and the system used a deplorable collections of old leased cars. The cars were ten years old and had been badly maintained with broken steam heating systems, inoperative air conditioners, loose seats, shuttered windows, and busted pipes. A large number of train stations had the appearance of a building in a poor neighborhood owned by an absentee owner.

Roger Lewis was the first president of Amtrak and found that angry employees were from railroads as Penn Central, the Burlington Northern, and the notorious Southern Pacific that was bankrupt. The system was inefficient and did not have a computerized reservation system. The ticket agents did a poor job in handling Amtrak's daily contact with passengers and had a large number of passenger complaints. Conductors had bad attitudes, lines at the ticket windows were too long, credit cards were not accepted, dining cars and coaches were cold in the winter, and the dining cars usually ran out of food.

Every since Amtrak has existed it has lost money. Tracks, bridges, tunnels, and trains needed repair, and signaling devices needed to be replaced. Funding to Amtrak had always been small compared to highways and airports, but this should have been a stimulant to the law makers in Washington, DC to make changes from the past, get into the present, and move toward the future.

By 1990, Amtrak made more than $1.3 billion that was an all time record, and it came closer to paying its way than ever before. A few years later revenues were covering 72 percent of their costs. It carried

22.2 million passengers and set an all time record of more than six billion passenger miles eight record years in a row. Amtrak carried another 18 million riders on commuter trains it operated separate from its inter-city system with all traffic increasing.

Even with that success, the father, Bush's Republican Administration attempted to abolish Amtrak for four continuous years from fiscal years 1987 to 1991. Ross Clayton of the National Association of Railroad Passengers said, "the republican administration spent 73 percent of funds on aviation for five consecutive years." He also said, Amtrak would cover 100 percent of its cost by year 2000. It would re-establish itself with investment communities permitting them to borrow money to match federal funds for that purpose.

The Reagan administration tried to abolish Amtrak entirely, including the Metroliners. Clayton said, if Amtrak's Northeast corridor services were eliminated, riders would be forced to fly between Washington and New York. There were 4,200 passengers that traveled daily between New York and Washington with over a million and a half annual riderships. In 1985, Amtrak became the largest carrier. It carried more passengers between New York and Washington than either of two airplane shuttles. Additional airline flights would have been necessary each day during peak travel times to handle the passengers. It was physically impossible for the already overcrowded airports with planes leaving from Washington and New York to handle all of the passengers traveling by Amtrak, and new airport facilities were unlikely.

Amtrak experience in moving people should have been enough for the politicians to grant money to update the railroad system and trains to increase ridership even more.

An article written by Philip Longman in US News said, all old Amtrak systems are loosing money. Helping that are trains that are pressured to run long distance to appease key members of Congress who want train service in their home states for political reasons. Amtrak had 41 routes in 2000, but according to Amtrak analysis, 14 lost more money per passenger than the year before. Most of the losses were on trains that traveled at slow speeds for long distances causing a lost of hours of productive time for passengers. A majority of people that traveled the longer distance were people that were retired or other older people. Why would a business man or woman take a train that traveled slow over twisted tracks that were old?

The New York-Washington Metroliner loss $38.06 per passenger, Washington to Chicago $141.03, Orlando to Los Angeles $247.94, and from Chicago to Janesville, Wisconsin $482.93 per passenger.

Based on the long history trains have in this country, people have been conditioned to associate the train with long traveling time, uncomfortable seats on cars, and rough twisting rides with small dingy bathrooms on each end of the car. As soon as a person hears the word train, they can visualize an old train twisting down the track.

Amtrak tried to increase revenue by expanding its freight express business and mail contracts, but they had to compete with overnight freight delivered to the office or door. They put on a train between Chicago and Janesville, Wisconsin to go after freight business. It was not a success and it was when they were losing $482.93 per passenger.

That was a clear indication that the Presidents and Congress were not interest in transportation by train. Freeways, vehicles, airports, and airplanes had changed with large financial help, but what was so significant about rail travel that it did not need to change and get financial help? The same railroad tracks, bridges, tunnels, and trains had been used for years, yet it was perceived that it did not need updating and Congress did not care. It was like flying in a 1950 commerical airplane filled with passengers today in 2001.

Since 1971 Amtrak has never made a profit. What will help is fast new trains, the twisted tracks with joints removed with new rails, and money to repair the unsafe tunnels and grade crossings. Why would a person ride a train that has a history of being slow? And why would the government not give Amtrak some money?

The New Acela Amtrak

The word Acela is an amalgam of the words friendly accelerations and excellence. It has a new way of traveling in the Northeast Corridor that is efficient and safe with good environments and it is a train that can be safely maintained for passengers traveling. This is the right time for the Acela Amtrak train that made its inaugural run in 2001 and is now carrying passengers. You do not need to arrive at the train station an hour or three hours before departing time, but can walk on the train five minutes before the departing time. It does not depend on oil or oil producing nations like airplanes and vehicles for fuels. What will happen if oil is dramatically cut back or the precious oil runs out?

Looking at the new train at the railroad station, passengers and prospective passengers see an aerodynamically shaped train that has a look that says it is ready for a fast comfortable trip. It is a beautifully designed train showing a pretty gray color. Passengers looking at the train had the same feeling when they purchased their first new car, making it difficult to wait to board the train and begin their trip. One thing they noticed, it does not have wings, engines hanging from the wings, and has big windows who sizes are difficult to believe. You had booked by telephone for a confirmed seat that included seat and car number.

Passengers boarding the older trains waited until others had gotten off at their destination, then the waiting passengers were free to board. The Acela has variable message signs and electronics that provides efficiency for de-boarding and boarding of passengers. A sign outside the car's forward door lets the passengers know where to enter providing an orderly flow to empty seats that can be identified by easily seen numbers. They see the interior of a pretty coach with warm comfortable colors, pretty carpets on the floors, and a quietness with no movements that does not identify a train.

The distance between the seats is 42 inches with large size padded armrests, curtains bordering the windows, and individual reading lights. The seats are side-by-side with wide roomy storage space above convenient in height for all passengers. When you sit, you discover the extra leg room and there is no seatbelt or space for seatbelt signs. There are dampers on the seats that add more comfort by eliminating any possible vibrations cause by any movements of the train. The conductor uses a small computer that accepts credit cards or tickets illuminating the indicator automatically that registers seat occupancy.

As you look out the wide long windows you realize there will be no orders from an antendant to remain in your seats. You are free to walk around at anytime without holding onto something for support because the ride will be smooth with no-side-to-side movements. Doors separating the cars open without a touch and everything is clearly marked. The former gloomy bath rooms are gone and the new ones are spacious and roomy with clean shiny back lighting in the mirror that offers a bright reflection. The sink has generous water pressure, paper cups, and plenty of paper towels.

You also discover there is a flat electrical panel facing each seat that permits travelers to place phone call via the train's telecommunications center, transmit documents to anywhere, and electrical plugs. The passengers are their boss and they have a flip switch that turns on a television with many channels as well as the CNN news. It feature's an extra large variety of programs from soap operas, soccer, cooking shows, and the Celtics if you are traveling at that time of year. Passengers can sit at any of the 32 conference tables throughout the train in swivel seats and the conductor's office includes displays that show the status of all connecting trains.

First class seats are wider than business class, but they both feature the same clever tray table instead of the dropdown tables on airplanes. There is more room with two and one seating with tinted glass providing semi-privacy. Four business class cars seat 64 passengers each and the first class coach seats 44 reserved and assigned. The train staff has new designed uniforms with the train's new corporate logo with parallel lines merging.

When the Acela moves forward there is no jerk. The forward movement is smooth, quiet, and when you look out the big window, it verifies the trains movements. As you continued to look out the window, the outside building seem to be passing and you wonder what the fast speed of 150 mph will be like.

There are no attendants pushing a cart down the wide aisle giving you small sacks of bagels in difficult to open bags. The dining car is designed more like a first class cafe with public seating areas, a television, and a stack of free New York Times newspapers. When you sit at the dining table, you are given menus with three choices for breakfast. There is fruit, Swiss cheese omelet with sausage, and home fries or pancakes with smoked apple chicken sausage. Another of the choices is a bagel, cream cheese, strawberry butter, a fruit plate, and you use real silverware associated with cloth napkins to clean your hands and wipe your mouth. If you do not feel like walking to the dinning room, your meal will be brought to you steaming hot carried by an attendant with a warm smiling face.

One of the meals for dinner is a southwestern pork tenderloin or a raspberry turkey sandwich, nicosia salad, and chicken caesar salad all priced between $6.95 and $7.95.

Other food offered on Acela Amtrak:

1. Pancakes with smoked apple chicken sausage steaming hot.
2. A dinner served with grilled rib-eye steak and butter, red skin whole or mashed potatoes, or a choice of rotisserie breast of chicken with corn cakes, pan-sears Chile shrimp with pesto pasta, and a selection of two wines.

There is a double decker called the family compartment car. Children are busy playing in the nursery with toys in the play area and other's just sit and stare in an unfamiliar environment. There are colors that help a parent or passenger remember which car they were riding in when they return to their seats.

No matter what cars you are seated in, the passengers will be near a big window decorated with curtains. Then you remember the small undersize windows on the airplanes, and as you look out the window, you realize the train is quietly moving. It is almost like the train is stationary and the objects outside are moving by. You do not notice the movement because the ride is smooth. Again you wonder what it will be like when the train reaches 150 mph. When it does, the conductor announces that the Acela has reached its top speed of 150 mph and then you recall the train at the station that looked liked it was ready to travel. At that speed, objects relatively close to the train window are almost a blur and you realize that if you were not looking out the window there would be no way of accessing the present.

When all 20 trains are delivered to Amtrak from the manufacturer, the express trains will continue to achieve a top speed of 135 mph service to Washington and New York with 19 weekday roundtrips. New York to Boston will have 8 daily roundtrips with a top speed of 150 mph, but weekends will feature fewer roundtrips. Acela Amtrak rewards enables members to earn points for free travel on board Amtrak, and transfer points for flights on United, Continental, and Midwest Airline Express.

Acela and Its Amenities

Since January 1, 2001, a passenger could rent a car from Hertz at a discount. They could earn points when they stayed at any participating Honors Hotels including Hilton, Conrad Hampton International, Hampton Inn, Suites at Hilton Garden Inn, Wood Suites and others. They can also redeem points for gift certificates from retailers and restaurants including Barnes & Nobles, Eddie Bauer, and Macy's. New members will receive 400 points for enrolling and traveling within 90 days and will also receive a permanent personal ID number upon enrollment that can be used immediately to begin earning points.

Three airlines based in the United States promoted travel on fast Supertrains overseas. Pan American and World Airways ran advertisements in major American newspapers promoting a tour package in France under a headline with a picture of the French steel wheel TGV train. The offer quotes included a trip on one of the world's fastest and most sophisticated trains. Timothy P. Gardner wanted to offer a package on the Amtrak allowing travelers to combine air and train travel at a price competitive with existing round-trip airline excursion fares.

The Acela has new electric horsepower engines, HHL, and one 6,616 hp engine on each end of the train for a fast comfortable ride. There will also be 20 new tilting Bombardier-built train-sets, and the train will have a capacity for 300 people.

In traveling around curves, the lateral forces on a conventional train tended to hold the wheels over the outer rails. As the wheels rolled into a curve there was little or no space between the wheel flange on the outside rail, consequently the wheels on the track would start to lift. It was one of the things that caused a train to leave the track if traveling to fast. As the frictional forces increased with the probability of a wheel climb, possible rail turnover and lateral buckling of the track increased, thus there was a limited amount of speed on curves with excessive friction and binding on the wheel assemblies.

The same forces are on the wheels and track of the Acela, but to prevent some dangerous forces at 125 mph or less, it employs self-steering wheel assemblies. Soft rubber elements holding the axles enable them to follow curves instead of remaining rigid. Centrifugal forces generated on curves would also be uncomfortable for passengers without that design. The system consist of computerized sensors that actuate hydraulic cylinders and tilt the car bodies for greater comfort. A new pneumatic suspension between each of the cars smooth the ride. It takes complete advantage of the tilt system which was designed to keep passengers comfortably in their seats or controlled when walking as the trains travels around curves. It will be limited to a tilt of 4.2 degrees rather than a maximum 6.8 degrees because the train coaches were made a little wider than normal.

In the 1930 The Timken Roller Bearing Company hired four young women to pull the Northern Pacific Locomotive No 1111, built by the American Locomotive Company. Despite the locomotive's weight of 355.7 tones, they pulled it. Because the Acela train rolls on steel rails with their joints welded together, the train is quiet, smooth with little resistance.

The steel wheel French TGV (*train a grande vitesse)* originated with the Bombardier/GEC Alsthom consortium. The group won the contract for Acela Amtrak, 20 train sets, and 15 HHL engines because it was willing to help finance the purchase on existing tracks and signed a 20 year service contract sharing information. Amtrak officials asked what were the three things they would do more of and what were the three things they would never redo in the train's design.

There is a new signal called the Advanced Speed Enforcement System. A signal in the cab of the train was developed by the consulting firm Parson Brienkerhoff. It uses and additional frequency on the rails and passive transponders along the track to provide five additional clear speed limits at 45, 60, 80, 100, 150 mph, and enforcement of permanent speed restrictions necessary for curves. The line-side-cable signal setup will continue to function, but will only be able to show clear 125 mph maximum approach to medium. It also provides positive-stop enforcement with penalty brake applications, even at restricted speeds. If an engineer fails to acknowledge a systems status change to a lower speed limit, he will be told to reduce the speed.

Taylor devised a kit of parts-pylons, gate identifiers, and destination platform signals where components are spaced above the platform. New lighting from fixtures will began to move in the direction the train is going before it arrives and there will be clear destination signs overhead.

Electrification of Line

Back in 1988, James P. RePass founded the National Corridor Initiative. Using his ideas and help from both party politicians, his company started electrifying the track from Connecticut to New York. The track from Connecticut to Boston was not electrified.

Nine high-speed corridors are:

1. Empire Corridor: Connecticut, Buffalo, Albany, and New York City.
2. Keystone Corridor: Connecticut, Philadelphia, and Harrisburg, PA.
3. Southeast Corridor: Connecticut, Washington, DC with Atlanta and Macon, GA on one line and Jacksonville, FL on another.
4. Gulf Coast Corridor: Connecticut, New Orleans with Houston to the West, Birmingham, AL to the North, and Mobile, AL to the East.
5. Florida Corridor: Connecticut, Tampa, Orlando, and Miami.
6. Midwest Corridor: Chicago to Cincinnati, Detroit, Milwaukee, Minneapolis, St. Paul, and St. Louis, MO
7. Pacific Northwest Corridor: Vancouver, British Columbia to Eugene, OR passing through Portland, OR, and Seattle, WA.
8. California Corridor: Sacramento and San Francisco, Los Angeles and San Diego,
9. Northeast Corridor: Boston, Connecticut., New Your, and Washington, DC.

Amtrak trains were pulled by diesel locomotive north of New Haven Connecticut because there were no electric lines. Electrification of the line from Connecticut to New York offered faster traveling times with electrified locomotives and it was Amtrak's dream to increase the speed between Boston and New York to 150 mph reducing travel time to approximately two hours between the cities. In updating the railroad system, two hundred fifty eight bridges were built in or before 1895 between Boston and Washington with much of the infrastructure not working. The system had other problems also.

The 231 miles between Boston and New York had a top-speed of 90 mph. The route weaved and twisted and the time from Boston to

New York was 4-1/2 hours. If an Amtrak train reached a time under three hours, it was estimated that it would take a third of the business from the airlines.

At that time there was a twenty minute locomotive change at New Haven. Every train going north from Connecticut was forced to stop 20 minutes in New Haven, Connecticut, shut down, and change from an electric to a diesel engine or vice versa when traveling south. Passengers sat in the cold darkness in the winter and hot cars in the summer waiting for the bump of the new engine indicating that the trip was ready to proceed. It had one good purpose and two bad. It was good for smokers and bad for passengers in hot cars in the summers and cold cars in the winter.

Amtrak employed a company based in Idaho that was a construction giant behind the Hoover Dam and the Alaskan pipe line to electrify the line. The name of the company was Nirrusib-Knudsen. After the contract was signed and time on the job, the company stopped construction because of financial problems and Amtrak hired Balfor Beaty Construction which is a British firm that had built a tunnel in Europe that collapsed in 1994. Beaty increased the original price from $321 million to $680 million. The reason, the original price was to low. Once a second contractor was interested in a job, there was not much that could be done since the job had to be completed.

Amtrak had built tracks for a speed of 125 mph and could adapt its system for a track that would be good for higher speeds. An extra large track-laying machine upgraded the Northeast Corridor. It removed the old rails and ties, plowed away the ballast, laid new concrete ties, and placed new rails on top that were continuous in one operation for a smooth quiet ride. The machine completed the tasks at a rate of 1,200 feet per hour with laser-alignment precision. Amtrak paid $200,000 to families whose sleep was interrupted by the glare of lights of welders working through the night. Joints at the rail ends were welded together.

Amtrak improved the tracks with a job of hanging high-powered electrical lines overhead along the entire route between Boston and New Haven with 15,000 poles, 70,000 feet of fencing, and a series of new power stations. Amtrak said the metal poles and wires would not really affect views to the water and beaches and promised to space the steel poles 200 feet apart. Some of the 30 foot high poles were 160 feet apart that transformed parts of the New England coast into an uninterrupted high-voltage eyesore.

High-speed trains like the Acela Amtrak can offer real advantages that aircraft cannot match. One is all weather reliability. Officials at Massport, which operates Boston's Logan International Airport said, traffic at the airport will double by the year 2010 and suggested using the Acela Amtrak line to New York like the first regular scheduled commercial flights established in 1927 between Boston and New York.

Wisconsin Governor Tommy Thompson, chairman of Amtrak's board of directors said, he hopes a fast start by the Acela Express will persuade Congress to pass a bill that will provide $10 billion in bonding for rail improvements that could bring high speed service to routes as Chicago-St. Louis, Seattle-Portland, OR, Dallas-San Antonio, and Los Angeles-San Diego.

The Paradox of Terrorist Attack

There is always a paradox to some event or something with contradictory results. When fertilizer appeared on the market, it was used all over the world to increase the growth of crops, but ground water runoffs were poisoning our water and killing our fish. That had not been considered. The terrorist attack killed many people, caused much suffering, money losses, and terror, but it caused a lot of people to take a train.

The canceled flights, waiting time, trip time, and airlines cutting their shuttle trips from 17 per day to four and fear, caused many people to take the Amtrak and Acela Amtrak trains to their destinations. The Acela Amtrak had been carrying passengers for nine months and with the increase in riders, more trains were being added. After the attack, ridership on the new Acela Amtrak increased over 40 percent because of the fear of flying, lost of time at the airports, and the reduction in schedules. The ridership also increased 15 percent on long distance rides said Michael S. Dukakis, chairman of Amtrak's board of directors at that time. He said, the trains will continue to sell out. There is no lost in time before the trip begins and in big business it is required to provide a dependable service.

Weather reliability can never be improved for airplanes thus providing an advantage for the Acela and other fast trains when they are operational. Even aviation reluctantly sees the necessity of high-speed trains or Supertrains. Some airlines were given permission to fly short flights that should have been reserved for high-speed trains. Runways and airports cost more money and has to many disadvantages. Canceled flights are covered up and airlines are not wise enough to realized the European countries are using trains integrated with airlines.

Even though the US was behind in rail transportation and knew the need, it did not give Amtrak $40 billion. However it gave the Pentagon $40 billion and $50 billion not including billions of dollars for the weapons systems. Similar amounts went to highways, aviation, and NASA.

In the 1960s, European Countries looked ahead and began providing high speed rail service between major cities. They planned to build trains for trips that traveled a distance of 350 miles or less realizing it would cost over $100 billion by the projected year of 2000. Washington, in their backward thinking, grudgingly invested $2.4 billion knowing Amtrak was still operating on tracks owned by the freight railroads.

Need for Commuter-Rail

The transportation system needed and need to integrate with the train. The terrorist attack gave a big push of travelers, but the transportation systems are still outdated. Steel-Wheel fast trains have a top speed of 150 mph and over and new maglev trains being built travel 300 mph with a 100 percent safety record over million of miles with no cancellation, waiting, crowded seats, no checkpoints, and long trip times. The congestion, smog, cost, and lost of time for the vehicle is prohibited. The airplane will still be convenient for long flights, but a new magnetic levitation train on a 1,500 mile trip can make the trip in approximately six hours with the total trip time a little over six hours. The ride would be smooth, quiet with no turbulent, and plenty of leg room in a good atmosphere. The total trip time on an airplane should not be much under that time depending on the time loss waiting at the airport.

Urban areas, crowded highways, and congested streets cannot be completely blamed on the American people nor on the growing population and number of vehicles. Growth gets some credit, but Washington, DC, the transportation planners, the engineers, and a lack of progressive plans deserve most of the blame. When the past, present, and estimated future is analyzed, it clearly advertises that everything will continue to grow. Realizing our transportation system is flawed and we cannot keep up with the pace, we must look at other ways that will help solve the problems and that is where the planners falter.

It can easily be seen that commuter-rails for inter-city travel is a demanded priority and has been for years in the past. One commuter-rail and longer distance trains can carry 300 passengers which is equivalent to 300 vehicles stuck in traffic. The same right-of-ways can be used pass the 21 century by adding more trains and adding more schedules without using more of our dwindling land. Politics will play a big part of our transition.

Using trains like the Acela Amtrak, approximately 70 million vehicle-miles would be trimmed from the region's trips each year resulting in reduced tailpipe pollutants by thousands of tons and saving million of gallons in fuel, death, and injuries. Estimates just in the Las Vegas to Southern California corridor alone would have a fuel reduction of 17 percent. Instead, the United States continues to build more facilities for vehicles and airplane jetliners, helping intensify dependence on the inefficient fuel deficient vehicles. Fredericksburg, Virginia, called for a national moratorium on paving. No new roads or parking lots should be built until the nation graduates from the over dependency of petroleum. The Senate Maglev Committee reports confirmed the new magnetic-levitation trains are far more efficient than vehicles and airplanes. In a petroleum-based transport economy, it is twice as efficient as vehicles and four times as efficient as airplanes.

Washington should be thinking about how Supertrains can help ease congestion by integrating millions of travelers from roads and airplanes. New highways, no matter how modern between cities, the top speed is listed as 65 mph, but the vehicle usually travels and average speed of 35 mph during peak traffic hours. A Supertrain or maglev system can be built at less cost, space, and move 300 passengers at 300 mph on one train. Train schedules can be changed to move more passengers in a shorter time period.

Some major Routes in the urban areas of Boston, Massachusetts are 2, 3, I-93, I-95, and I-495. Traffic in peak hours on Route 3 for approximately 20 miles is delayed by at least 2-1/2 hours per person going and returning making five hours total. Construction began in the spring of 2001 adding one lane in both direction in an attempt to eliminated the problems. Traffic going from Massachusetts to New Hampshire will get some relief even at congested areas because the New Hampshire road will have three lanes all the way.

Inner-state I-95 in Massachusetts is already stop and go causing a backup on Route 3 just to get on I-95 going in either direction. A new lane will only cause more vehicles to back up on Route 3. Help for now and the future could be realized by installation of a commuter-rail down Route 3 from New Hampshire to I-95 In Massachusetts. Two overpasses from Route 3 could connect to a commuter-rail going in either direction on I-95. The commuter-rail going North would connect to the station in Woburn.

It has been stated that the widening of bridges for the new lanes on Route 3 will be wide enough for another lane to be added for the future. The authorities already realize the new lanes will only be temporary for moving increased traffic flows to Massachusetts.

However, the extra space under existing bridges could be better used for a commuter rail.

A rail system is anticipated from Merrimack, NH to Lowell where it will connect with a train with standing room only to Boston. The existing rails by the Merrimack river will be used instead of a new one adjoining Route 3.

Texas and Arizonia also have ideal terrain for trains, but it would be much easier if train tracks were plannned with the building of urban settlements and access to the cluster of businesses using high-speed rail a long side the freeways. Using a right-away of 300 feet for freeways could easily be widen to include a 30 foot right-away for a train or trains. With smart planning and future thoughts, large amounts of money and time can be saved. This would move people faster and still provide a roadway for use in off peak hours, necessities, or for short distances with less use of petroleum.

Blame and responsibilities are totally on the past Presidents and Congress. Aggressive lobbyist from the airlines, NASA, highways, gasoline companies, auto makers, and others persuaded the policy makers to withhold large sums of money from the train companies. It was totally political because even the politicians could see a need for fast trains.

Railroad Lines Promised Help

Before the terrorist attack in September, 2001, two politicians were wiser and realizing trains were a necessity for helping our transportation systems. Chairman of the House Transportation Committee, United States Representative Don Young of Alaska and a senior Republican submitted a bill offering $71 billion to fund the creation of a "nationwide" high-speed rail system. It would be available to states for laying new tracks, elevated crossings in cities, repair of bridges, tunnels, new signaling devices, other improvements to sustain train speeds of 125 mph and faster, and commuter-rails for inter-city travel.

Legislation will separate the future of high-speed rail service from the future of Amtrak which is struggling to meet a 2003 deadline to end its reliance on annual federal operating subsidies. The transition to Amtrak after the terrorist attack will help, but the bill will provide $36 billion in tax-exempt bonds and $35 billion in loans and loan guarantees over ten years Steve Hanson said. Amtrak cannot apply for funding.

This bill has no continuity and is lacking in thought that will create a segregated transportation system with a lost of money. A part of our rail system broken into regions is wrong. We need a national program opposed to a disjointed regional transportation system. The High-Speed Rail Investment Act has been endorsed by 184 members of the House of Representative, 57 Senators, the National Governors Association, the US Conference of Mayors, and dozens of business and community groups precisely because passenger rail is a national interest not a regional interest. High-speed rail does not make sense in a few regions and it is not meeting a national interest. When the inter-state roads were built, it was a complete federal effort providing a vehicle life line for all cities and towns.

We have to connect cities by high-speed rail to serve less populated regions along the routes and provide a transportation that serves all people. Amtrak is trying to achieve operational self-sufficiency even though it is part of a national system and the only transportation system required to be independently self sufficient. What good could come from a systems that is divided with different infrastructures and operations? What good would it serve to have separate federal agencies that oversee separate train operations?

Living in the year of 2001, the only plausible reason could be since many of the politicians do not like Amtrak and at least two Presidents tried to end its life, there must be a better reason. Maybe that is the only way the high-speed rail system could get any money and as time passes, maybe the money will be used on a national transportation system including Amtrak.

Now the required cost for transportation by train is much higher than it would have been thirty years ago, but some policy makers finally saw the need. Amtrak estimates that upgrading 11 federally designated high-speed corridors will cost $50 to $70 billion.

Past experiences indicate Congress is not good at long or short term planning. They are to wrapped up in present things guided by lobbyist and do not generate an effort that requires common sense, foresight, visions, and do not even take time to plan for an obvious future. It took strong imaginations, conjectures, and many sets of visions to convince board members to build 42,000 miles of inter-state highway systems and build expensive airports to stimulate commerical aviation. The inter-state highways required right-of-ways, large amounts of money, created congestion, and took lush real estate where farmers grew crops for Americans to eat.

Since the golden spike completed the transcontinental railroad in 1859, railroad systems have been built and used all across America. Complete new systems do not need to be built, but Congress will not even give the railroads funds to repair the outdated and deplorable railroads and buy new efficient trains that the public needs. The new Acela Amtrak and other Amtrak trains are being blamed for not being on schedules and not reducing travel times, yet they are forced to use old railroads and travel over bridges built in the 1800s. Congress does not see that the rail network needs modernize rail, electrical systems, repair of tunnels, electrical lines, replacement of faulty equipment, straighten railroads, bridge repair, and protection against mud and rockslides.

Concrete ties need to replace wooden ties where spikes move up and down in the wooden ties, welded rail joints to add quietness, and new maglev trains that float above guideways for comfort, speed, and safety. The United States has sent man to the moon, has fighter planes that reach speeds over 1,800 mph, new commerical planes that fly our skies, and spy satellites that see well, but we lag the foreign countries in rail transportation and really are not concern.

Amtrak is aggressively requesting an emergency $3.2 billion package from Congress to help crumbling infrastructure. Without being asked, Congress is giving billions to airlines. Not because of their service, but because of less service.

Cost of Airports vs Train Transportation

As airplane populations continue to grow and the positives new runways are suppose to provide will be overcome by the numbers as more airplanes are built and land at airports.

Hong Kong's airport opened in 1997 and cost over $4.5 billion not counting costs of new access roads. Spending for a new airport in Seoul reached over $5 billion and a new Chicago airport would reach approximately $5 billion. What would help is a train system that extended into the future. Our Transportation System is still living in the past and believe building more airports will solve our transportation problems. What we really need is integration with the airports and high-speed trains where either can be boarded at the same terminal. With all of the information available and more new planes on order, industry will work to make sure that more runways are built rather than look at the past information and try to catch up to the systems in Europe. Spending over $8 billion per year for existing airports and their upkeep will not solve the problems.

Atlantic, Boston, Chicago, Las Vegas, and Austin, Texas could relieve airport congestion by using Supertrain lines as suggested by engineers and economist at the Argonne National Laboratory. They have the ideal terrain for guideways or for high-speed-rail.

The public will encounter greater costs, diminished conveniences, and quality of service if strategies are not planned now that take action in the developing of domestic travel needs. Congestion on highways and airports waste time, fuel, and increases pollution. Adding more highway lanes and building new airports in or near the larger cities is becoming increasingly difficult and land is costly and scarce now. What will the conditions be like ten years from now?

Adding new highway capacity in urban areas typically costs more than $15 million per lane-mile. That's $45 million for three lanes per mile and $60 million for four lanes per mile. Sixty million dollars will pay the cost for 19 miles of new railroads for a steel-wheel train, much less using existing right-of-ways. Three and one half miles of elevated guideways can be built at that price for a new maglev train that has a perfect safety record and travel's at 300 mph. It can continue to handle numbers of people years into the future. All that will be needed is additional schedules and or adding more train cars.

The continuation of the exclusive reliance on flying and driving will continue to generate environmental problems and constrain capacities even further causing more gridlock and winglock. Aviation and highway transportation technologies are petroleum dependent, accounting for 64 percent of total petroleum used, 38.5 percent above US petroleum production contributing to the United States trade deficit, and dependence on oil imports with national security implications.

A Competitive Trip Plane vs Train

A competitive trip was taken from a New York hotel by two men for first arrival at Post Office Square in Boston. One left their hotel at 7:30 a.m. in a cab going to the LaGuardia airport. After he arrived at the airport, he had two cancellations, a runway temporally closed, and was shuttled from one airplane to another. He took off at 10:47 a.m. and arrived in Boston where he took a cab to Post Office Square from Logan Airport for $20. He arrived and had his ticket stamped at the parking lot at 11:45 a.m.

The second gentleman left the same hotel in a cab at the same time and arrived at Penn Station at 7:34 a.m. He boarded the Acela train at 7:56 a.m. and left Penn Station two minutes late of the schedule time. At 9:30 a.m. the Acela made its first stop at New Haven, CT, reached a speed of 150 mph, and reached its destination at

South Station and arrived at Post Office Square in a cab. His ticket was stamped at the same parking lot at 11.47 a.m. It took the train two minutes longer than the airplane.

Naturally the airplane had less air travel time, but the whole trip was shorter by only two minutes. The person on the airplane had some problems with delays, but this is what a person has to tolerate because there is no valid assumption that the airplane will not be delayed for any number of reasons. But the conditions of the person's mind played an important part on the trip with anxiety. The person on the train had a relaxed ride with no instructions on the trip. These are some of the things a person must consider when traveling.

Chapter 7: Monorail & Steel-Wheel Trains

Monorail

The Metropolitan Transportation Authority (MBTA) asked Jack Bradury to speak on regional transit problems forty years ago. No friends were made when he said, this $500 million MBTA headquarters we are in has to go. It is ridiculous he said, "You could build a transit system for the cost of putting this place up." He also called for a monorail system in Los Angeles, California. He was put out of the meeting and Los Angeles purchased buses. There was a failure of imagination and a failure for transportation.

San Francisco was the first in the US to have a monorail system. It was built in 1962 for the World's Fair. Thirty five years later in 1997, the voters voted for a monorail running a distance of 42 miles to four difference locations across the city. It could be elevated above the streets more easily since it is lighter in weight than a rail system, but the major money was used to build more roads and purchase light-rail systems. Business men did not like the possibility of people riding the monorail above their businesses rather than driving vehicles or riding buses by their shops. They visualized more business if the vehicles drove down the streets with the occupants being stimulated by the unique displays in a buying atmosphere.

A monorail is a single rail serving as a track for a train with rubber wheels on each sides of the train and track. It travels on an over-head system similar to conventional trains, but is quiet.

It uses powerful electric motors and better computerized suspension systems. The vertical support pillars are spaced at approximately 100 feet apart in a leading model from the Montreal-based maker, Bombardier. Previously there was awkward switching from one track to another, but Bombardier can now switch tracks in 8 to 12 seconds.

Residents proposed a new light-rail system for the Cincinnati, Ohio metropolitan area. They became angry because the light-rail vehicles they had approved could not climb the grade to the regional airport on their side of the Ohio River. Residents that live in Covington, Kentucky on that side of the river were pressing for a switch to monorail whose rubber tires and enclosed guideways provided better traction than steel-wheeled light-rail vehicles. They persuaded their congressman, Jim Bunning, to arrange federal funding to study the monorail system.

Seattle invested in down town monorail systems that quickly became favorites with tourists and locals. Last November in 2000, Seattle voters approved a fast mass transit. But that bright vision was eclipsed by a surge of highway building and a rush to build urban light-rail systems. Monorail was written off as a novelty. It was good for Disneyland, but hardly a serious option for the metropolitan area.

Las Vegas became interested in Newark International Airport transportation system, which offers passengers a monorail link between airline terminals. The Disney theme parks in Florida and California shuttled a large number of people daily on a monorail system.

Transportation Secretary Kevin Sultan has directed the Massachusetts Bay Transportation Authority to study a proposal to build a monorail linking the two rail hubs. He directed the MBTA General Manager to set up a task force. It can be an untapped resource, which could prove cost effective, reliable, and buildable said Kevin Sultan. A monorail system would offer clean, noiseless, fast, and smooth rides making on time connections.

When planners plan Routes, it is necessary that they are located in areas where needed and convenient for travelers. The terms High-Speed, Supertrains or Bullet Trains are used to describe any rail systems capable of speed at or exceeding 125 mph. Other than a maglev train, they have no equals whatsoever in transporting numbers of people in comfort, convenience, reliability, and safety. They have never had a passenger fatality.

Japan had eight urban monorails and leads the world in elevated transit. Their trains have reached 323 mph, would cost at least $5 billion to build by 2020, and are projected to reach millions of passengers per day, generating annual revenues in the high millions. Vancouver, Sidney, Brazil, Singapore, and parks in South Koreas also have monorail trains.

Countries with High Speed Steel-Wheel Trains

Congestion and pollution in many countries are so bad that politicians are compelled to try and restrain road traffic by price or regulation. More and more countries are looking to restrain the use of cars by levying road-user charges with electronic road-pricing systems as urban congestion gets worse. The economic balance is beginning to shift.

Traffic on all of American expressways have slowed to a crawl during rush hours every day. Over 100 million Americans live in cities, where vehicle emissions regularly exceed federal health standards. Switzerland has banned all loaded vehicles over a certain weight from crossing the Alps, France prohibits heavy vehicles on motorways on Sundays, and many Italian cities exclude cars from their central areas. By 2004, all through-freight across the Swiss Alps will have to be carried by rail.

The airplane and the automobile revolutionized travel, but now we have began to experience limits of technology, environment, and capacity all over the industrialized world. To meet part of the growth in transportation demands, governments have invested funds into reinventing the transportation technology and the steel-wheel railroad system. The steel-wheel train of the early century had technical limits for higher speeds, unstable wheel-bogie dynamics, limited traction, wear and vibration-induced fatigue failures causing high maintenance, ride discomfort for the passengers, and excessive noise.

Efforts to improve passenger rail technology in the United States was slowed by the building of the Boeing 707. The growth of air travel decreased inter-city rail usage as well as the new interstate highway systems. However, other industrialized countries began to make improvements in steel-wheel rail transportation by the 1960s over 41 years ago and continue to make improvements.

Some countries are:

1. China	3. Japan	5. Italy	7. France	9. Norway	11. Spain
2. Taiwan	4. Russia	6. Germany	8. Switzerland	10. United States	

China is planning a high-speed-rail system 812 miles long linking Beijing and Shanghai that should be completed by 2010. The trains will operate at a speed of 155 mph and later at 217 mph reducing the travel time from 17 hours to approximately 6 to 7 hours. France, Japan, and Germany are competing to supply the trains and technology. Japan lost to France for the South Korean transportation system, so it is very interested. Japan will also provide loans to China if it uses their "bullet train" technology.

China plans to construct approximately 4,900 miles of high-speed systems creating a potential for a large China market. China's Premier Zhu Rongji wants to experience an 18 mile ride to the airport at a speed of 267 mph on a French Transrapid maglev train by 2003. Beijing's deputy mayor wants the route between downtown Beijing and the main airport to be built for trains that travel at speeds 74 to 124 mph. Speeds that slow will make a steel-wheel train much cheaper than the maglev train. The competitors for supplying the trains are Germany and Japan.

Taiwan is building a high-speed system that should be in operation by 2003 on the country's western corridor where 95 percent of Taiwan's 21.5 million people live. The affluent population is crowded on the transportations north-south network that consist of highways, a freeway, a narrow-gauge railway, and an air transport system. The trains will carry 800 to 1,100 passengers, and 1,100 to

1,400 passengers on double decker units. They will travel between Taipei and Kaohsiung at speeds of approximately 155 to 186 mph. A European consortium led by Siemens and GEC Alsthom was just awarded a contract to build a $13.4 billion high-speed line in Taiwan.

Japan has operated the bullet train since 1950, but is now introducing new designs. One system is the 400-Series mini shinkansen that runs on upgraded conventional rails converted from narrow gauge to shinkansen standard gauge with a top speed of 148 mph on shinkansen lines and 80 mph on conventional lines.

The fastest steel-wheel train in Japanese service has a maximum speed of 186 mph and is a 500-Series that went into service in 1997. An 8-car double-deck shinkansen called the E4 is in operation now, but the 700-Series is the new generation of shinkansen. It was jointly designed by a manufacturing company named JR Central and JR West for use on both Sanyo Shinkansen and Tokaido lines. It travels 167 mph on the Tokaido tracks and 186 mph on the Sanyo tracks. Trains that travel at a speed of 217 mph are expected to be operational by 2007.

Japan's shinkansen has been operating over 34 years between Tokyo and Osaka, a distance of 312 miles and has carried more than "3 billion" passengers without any fatalities. Even with delays caused by earthquakes, rain or snow, the average deviation from schedule was only 36 seconds per train. During peak hours, 11 trains leaving in each direction carried a total of 368,000 passengers per day. Still with an eye on the demand for the future, Japan plans to raise the rush-hour frequency to one train every four minutes. A new Series 300 train cruises at 170 mph and will reduced the time from Tokyo to Osaka by 15 minutes.

Japan introduced a double-deck high-speed train that carries 500-800 passengers making six times as many trains from Tokyo to Osaka as there are airline departures and increasing the market share to 84 percent. Three thousand maintenance workers do repairs when the rail operations close at night.

The shinkansen operations began in 1964 and not a single passenger has been killed on any express line in Japan. For comparison, if all of the passengers switched to car travel, the estimate would be at least 1,800 deaths and 10,000 serious injuries each year.

Heavy surface vehicles at higher speeds through populated areas create pressure waves. Sonic booms were triggered as the shinkansen entered tunnels. To handle that, cowls at tunnel entrances have been used in an effort to limit the disturbance. At their present speeds, they have to be expensively pressurized to prevent damage to passengers' eardrums. Prior unpressurised coaches caused a number of side-effects to passengers and several lavatories exploded.

The ER200 is a Russian-built steel-wheel train that travels between Moscow and St Petersburg at an average speed of 80 mph and is designed for a top speed of 124 mph. The ER200, named for its top speed (200 km/hour) makes only one round trip per week, is unreliable, and unprofitable. Russia also has a train called Sokol. It is a steel-wheel train that travels at an average speed of 160 mph carrying 800 passengers in 12 cars. Their hope is to have 30 trains running daily in each direction between Moscow and St. Petersburg by 2005.

The effort will be the largest civil engineering project since the collapse of the USSR. The work will include building 200 major bridges and laying 405 miles of new track. The new track is going through land that has been untouched since the end of World War II with unexploded bombs and mines still in the area. Environmentalists are against building the track a distance of 62 miles through a Nature Reserve unless it is constructed in an "environmentally-sensitive" manner.

Italy plans a steel-wheel system called Treno Alta Velocita (TAV) network that includes Milan, Rome, Naples north-south route with connection to Bari and Sicily, and an east-west Turin-Milan-Venice route to be completed in 2003. It will use ERT 460 tilt-trains and ERT 500 non-tilt trains on new high-speed and existing lines with a capability of 186 mph. A dedicated high-speed track was built from Rome to Naples and from Florence to Bologna.

Germany has an inter-city express (ICE) high-speed rail network. It was behind the main European countries when it began developing a network of high-speed railway lines. It now has its ICE's and is making up for lost time. The country's first high-speed railway lines were revealed in 1992 with steel-wheel trains that traveled from 155 mph to 174 mph. It is interesting to note that the United States steel-wheel train probably has a higher top speed than 150 mph, but the condition of the rail lines will not permit the train to travel faster.

Siemens of Germany developed and built 60 ICE-I trains that operated the first services and the network of lines on the ICE network as it continued to grow. Since 1997, they introduced the ICE-2, ICE-3, and ICE-T, which is a tilting train. Figure 7.1 shows the high-speed ICE-2 that has an appearance similar to the ICE-T.

Fig 7.1. ICE-2 high-speed train. Courtesy Deutsche Bahn

See figure 7.2 for an interior view of the ICE-3. It has a clear screen separating passengers from the engineer giving the passengers a clear exterior view enabling them to access the speed of the train.

Fig. 7.2. Clear screen on ICE-3 between passengers and engineer for accessing speed. Courtesy Deutsche Bahn.

The ICE-T was introduced and developed by the Siemens Transportation Systems. It has a top speed of 145 mph over smooth or rough terrain with electric or diesel versions and has improved passenger comforts. All three trains have expanded the network to include destinations to Switzerland, Holland, Austria, and Germany. The network is intended for travelers traveling up to 50 miles between stops.

As stated briefly in chapter 2, steel-wheels on conventional trains are mounted rigidly in bogies (a strongly built rigid assembly) shown in figure 7.3. The wheels assembly remain rigid and parallel to the car above them as the train moves through all curves. This generates powerful forces creating high temperatures on the rails and wheels and uncomfortable forces on the passengers.

To increase the safety, lower temperatures on the wheels and rails, and more comforts for the passengers at all speeds on curves, the tilting cars have a self-steering wheel assembly shown in figure 7.4. Elements holding each axle of each two steel wheels enables them to follow curves for greater passenger comforts and reduce the temperatures of the wheels and rails. To reduce the centrifugal forces generated, computerized sensors actuate hydraulic cylinders and tilt the bodies of the cars up to eight degrees and a pneumatic suspension between each of the cars shown in figure 7.5 smoothes the ride.

Fig. 7.3. Conventional Steering Truck. Courtesy Popular Science.

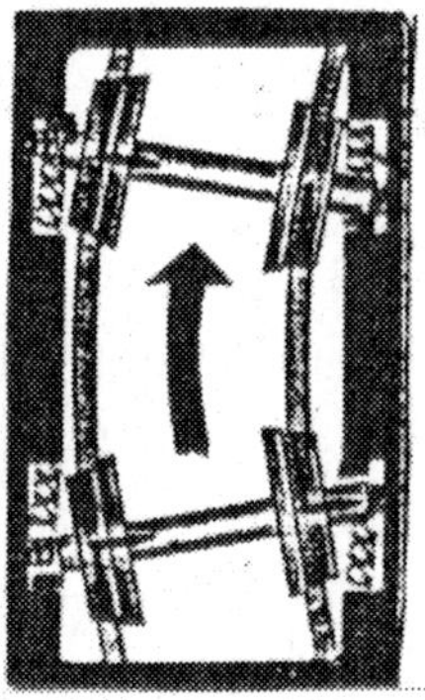

Fig. 7.4. Radial-Track. Courtesy Popular Science.

Fig. 7.5. Pneumatic Suspension. Courtesy Popular Science

France has been in the high-speed rail service since the 1970s and has a rail network that will accommodate steel-wheel trains traveling long distances at speeds in excess of 186 mph. The TGV (*trans a grande vilesse)* was to provide high-speed rail travel only to France, but because of its popularity, the network reaches into Belgium, Switzerland, Germany, and Italy.

Since a high-speed line opened in 1981, expansion has taken place between Paris and Lyon. Paris still remains the hub of the network, but the network has spread in all directions and provides quick and easy access to the French capital from all parts of the country and beyond. A rail line linking Paris and Strasbourg including Chalons sur Marine, Nancy and Bar Le duc is a 312 mile line. The travel time will be reduced from four and one quarter hours to two hours and nineteen minutes by 2006. The steel-wheel TGV with a cruising speed of 185 mph reduces the journey between Brussels and Paris to 85 minutes, a saving of over a half an hour.

France has a number of routes planned and one has international connections that include a 156 mile stretch between Lyon to Torino Italy. That includes a 31 mile tunnel under the Alps that will use the French steel-wheel TGV and the Italian steel-wheel ETR trains.

It is developing a new generation of steel-wheel TGV-NG trains that travel at speeds between 210 to 248 mph. Operating at those speeds requires technologies for aerodynamics, noise reduction, braking, and traction motors for passengers and people living near the rail lines.

Using lighter paints and electrical wires with thinner insulation, light weight materials, and better construction techniques are some of the things that will be used to reduce weight.

Others countries with fast steel-wheel trains are Switzerland, Norway, Spain, and the United States.

Trains are having a strong effect on the public's traveling habits and in some places air traffic has been affected negatively. This has influence the French government to further expand the network. Every TGV line built has covered its construction costs within a few years of operation making the network one of the most profitable elements of the system. Because of the success and the increase in passenger demands, double decker Duples TGV's are being built.

Their automatic train protection systems are designed to monitor and display line-side-signals in the train cab. They will intervene when needed and automatically apply brakes if a signal has not responded resulting in danger. Another factor of the activities at the depot is to make sure an adequate number of trains are at all locations at the beginning of each day.

Steel-Wheel Noise

Because of the train in rural communities, France reduced the disturbance caused by the noise of trains running at 186 mph.

However, the high levels of acoustic noise by these trains continues to be a problem. The promise of low noise and high speeds is one of the reasons Japanese maglev proponents use to justify continued maglev development. Matsumoto states trains have reached speeds in trials of 217 mph, but with excessive noise that will force operations at lower speeds.

High-speed rail uses low-weight equipment since energy costs are proportional to the weight of the car and to the cube of speed. Also aerodynamic effects are very important at high speeds.

The amplitude of a sound wave is related to the energy it carries. The greater the amplitude the greater the amount of energy it has and the greater the sound. Noise is an unwanted or undesirable sound.

Noise from a high speed rail system is generally dominated by three sources, mechanical structural noise sources, propulsion and auxiliary equipment, and airflows moving past the train. The sources differ in where they occur in the system and in what frequency range they dominate. The major noise from a train is between steel-wheel/rail and aerodynamic forces. The noise increases as speed increases.

The mechanical/structural noise sources are from the steel-wheel/rail interaction on conventional trains and vehicle body vibrations, even though the track structures are of continuous welded rails on concrete ties. The steel-wheel-rail reactions is the rolling noise steel-wheels and rails cause because of small rough elements in the top surfaces. High speed trains have smooth steel-wheel rails with no rail joints, and the transition speed is approximately 150 mph.

When the surfaces become rough, the steel-wheel/rail noise increases and the transition occurs at a higher speed than a system with smoother wheel-rails. This noise source is close to the trackbed and can be shielded by barriers.

As the wheels go over these surfaces they also cause vibrations in the rails and the wheels. This generates or transmits waves in the soil that passes through the soil or rocks until stopped by a buildings or limited distances.

The amount of vibration from the train depends on the type of rock, ground, or sand between the vibrating source and the element that receives the vibration. It is transmitted through Bedrock 10 meters from the surface and causes vibrations to propagate at greater distances. Vibrations also travel through clay, but because of the separation of the pieces of sand, the vibrations are damped out.

Propulsion noise sources are generated by trains powered by electric motors using fans to cool the equipment. They are the major source of noise and are located near the top of the cars picking up electric power from power lines that generate power to drive the train. Propulsion systems using fossil fuel generate noise from three systems: the power generating unit, electric traction motors that drive the wheels, and the alternator or alternators. The exhaust on top of the locomotive also radiates noise.

Aeroacoustic noise sources are generated from airflow over a train by flow separation and reattachment, turbulent boundary layers over the entire surface of the train, flow interactions with edges and appendages, and flow interactions between moving and stationary components of the system. These sources can be located over the entire surface of the train and at the edges of guideway structure.

Electric power is supplied to high speed trains from nearby substations near the tracks to the train via overhead suspended wires, or third rails running alongside the guidance rails. The electric current returns through the rails to complete the circuit.

Whenever current flows through a loop, an electromagnetic field (EMF) is formed within the loop and in a region around it. The magnitude of the magnetic field is proportional to the magnitude of the current in the loop and it oscillates corresponding to the frequency of the electrical current. At very high intensities, EMF hazards include electric shock, pacemaker interference, and burns, but the magnetic fields in the vicinity of transportation systems are classified as low intensity fields where the effects are not well known. Most of North America frequencies are 60 Hz and the magnetic fields near transportation systems oscillate at what is termed extremely low frequencies, ELF.

Magnetic fields are difficult to shield, making it difficult to reduce the effect. They penetrate our bodies and electrical fields concentrate on skin surfaces.

Problems With Tracks for Steel-Wheel Trains

In 1955, almost fifty years ago, France was testing a train at a speed of 205 mph with an interest for rail research. President Dwight Eisenhower in America was preparing to sign The Interstate Highway Act for vehicles competing with our railroad systems. America was not planning for the future, but being lobbied by the automobile makers, gasoline, and oil companies

A railroad is a permanent road having a line of two parallel rails secured to wooden or concrete ties and laid on a roadbed. This provides a track for cars or equipment pulled by a self-contained engine. The existing rails cause problems for high-speed steel-wheel trains at high speeds. The high-speed trains were built to reduce travel time, but the large cost of building new high-speed railways generated a new system for reducing time and providing comforts for the passengers on curves.

Since most systems' engineering and physical structures were designed for heavy freight trains, the rails were not able to support high-speed passenger trains. This led to a new way of using the old railways and reduced travel time rather than building costly new high-speed dedicated railways.

France invested in a complete update to enable trains with added stresses of regular use by trains traveling at high-speeds. To prolong the life of their track formations, strict axle weight limits are on the tracks in use. The steel-wheel-rail interface was one of the major factors in the everyday stresses on the rail tracks. The system now uses a magnetic induction braking system that bypasses that interface.

In 1998/99 an Alstom factory at Belfort, France, built a new train designed to use in any of the electrical specifications on European railways yet retained the essential benefits of the first generation of units. Each train had to be fitted with an interference current monitoring unit to measure the levels of electrical interference produced by the trains, and ensure that they did not exceed safe levels.

The design provided a high degree of stability at the highest speeds and reduced problems that caused track wear, keeping noise at acceptable levels. It was a modular train consisting of nine different modules including a mixture of single and double-deck vehicles.

A double track system would cost about $15 to $20 million per mile and that would include terminals, trains, and construction of guideways. By comparison, interstate highway segments often cost much more than that. New airports, if they can be built over public objections, are expected to cost as much as $5 billion each. That cost would provide a 250 mile doubletrack system without future winglock or gridlock with much less expensive upkeep.

Jack L. Duchemin was a transport expert in the Brussels-based Commission of the European Communities. He says the elimination of freight trains from the tracks increased safety and limited cost of track maintenance. This is why after nine years of experience, the French National Railway says, TGV high speed lines are less expensive to maintain than old existing lines that carried heavy freight on passenger lines.

Speed and economy of road transport have caused a decline in rail freight across the world. In Japan, rail's share of freight has dropped from 50 percent in 1955 to less than 5 percent. Continental Europe rail between 1970 and 1994 lost half of its 32 percent share of the freight market, and Britain's rail share declined from 42 percent in 1952 to only 6 percent now. America's has also lost a big percentage of their freight traffic.

Trains That Tilt On Curves

The tilt vehicle permitted one third faster speeds using accelerometers and gyroscopes to give advance warning of curves. A four hour trip from Milan to Basie on a Pendolino tilting train was very smooth. A glass of wine on a table hardly moved as the train traveled around curves and through the Alps at speeds up to 30 percent faster than normal. The Pendolino operates in the Czech Republic, Spain, Portugal, Germany, Finland, and Switzerland.

In Britain, there is a fleet of tilting trains that travel 140 mph, reducing travel time from London to Glasgow by a third. Sweden has the Adtranz X2000 tilting train that has raised the rail's share of the market compared to air travel from 41 percent to 55 percent. It reduced a 285-mile trip from Stockholm to Gothenburg nearly one quarter of the total time. France is a high-speed champion on dedicated track, but tested tilt trains for use on both high-speed and its conventional tracks.

Germany introduced its first inner-city express tilting trains in 1998 for diesel and electric versions with a top speed of 145 mph.

Tracks used for tilt trains only need a modest upgrading and cost about $500,000 a mile. That is about one twentieth the cost of a new dedicated high-speed track and about $24 million more than the price of a conventional train.

Integrated Tracks, New and Old

Certain times during the day or peak periods on the TGV trains, the fares are reduced to lower rates. The passenger gets a lower price using off-peak hours for traveling. The prices for travel on each day of the year is listed on a calendar coded in red, white, and blue which are the colors of the French national flag. Approximately 250 off-peak blue day reductions are made annually. White days are classified as standard and only lower fares are available. The highest priced days marked in red are for peak travel. This price difference helps control the influx of passengers, otherwise the system could not handle it.

Some TGV trains have an engine at each end of a 10-car long train and at busy times two trains coupled together can carry 1,100 riders and one set can carry 485 passengers. In comparing the numbers with an airplane, that's about the number of passengers in two jumbo jets. But the passengers ride in comfort on soft seats in the 10-car train with plenty of leg room.

The Atlantic TGV train in France travels over 177 miles on new tracks that link Paris to Courtalian. At Courtalain the track branches into Y-shape lines. One line connects with existing tracks and continue to other destinations. The other leg of the top part of the Y connects with existing lines to Bordeaux and Lourdes. Those tracks have been upgraded for a maximum speed of 136 mph. The improved tracks are compatible and integrate with the old network that enables the trains to travel into city centers providing wide territorial coverage using the conventional tracks. When the trains reach the countryside, they travel on the super-speed tracks.

America could follow the same proved pattern. Outside the cities in urban areas would be new high-speed lines, with existing tracks used to reach city and airport destinations.

Germany, Japan, and Europe have shown that high-speed railways can be profitable. Rail has the edge in safety, reliability, and speed over both cars and aircraft for travel up to 5 hours. With the help of the terrorist attack, the public learning process of the comforts of high-speed trains will continue to grow. It will become a popular necessity.

Chapter 8: Magnetic Levitation Trains

Maglev Trains

Maglev is used for Magnetic Levitation train and the first train theory was conceived by Emil Bachelet, a French engineer working in France in 1912. The system had an eddy-current repulsive levitation system. He built a small model, with electromagnets in the guideway that created eddy currents in an aluminum plate under the module. In another concept, electromagnets were carried as outboard winglets and generated eddy currents in two aluminum plates along the guideway.

He was not able to secure financial backing for implementation of his ideas and was so discouraged, he emigrated to the US and became a citizen of America. Now, his electromagnets are replaced with superconducting magnets which had not been designed at that time.

The development of high-current-density superconducting wire in the early 1960s created the age of maglev transportation. The first proposals for superconducting levitated vehicles was made by two physicists, Dr. James Powell and Dr. Gordon Danby of Brookhaven National Laboratories in Long Island, New York, in 1966.

While struck in a traffic-jam, Dr. James P. Powell had an idea. He and his colleague, Dr. Cordon T. Danby, thought of a way to transport people and cargo using a technology called magnetic levitation (maglev). What they visualized would rely on powerful magnets to suspend trains inches above a guideway and propel them friction-free and quiet at speeds up to 300 mph.

Powell and Dandy were not asking for long-term funding from the government, just money to get started. This type of priming is what happened with railroads, aviation, and the highway systems. It was at a time when the potential impact on the United States economy would have been a significant fraction of the nearly $1 "trillion" spent annually on all forms of transportation in this country. The economic incentives would have been constructive and operations of the high speed train systems would have provided thousands of jobs. Rail and train stations also encourage tourism, real estate development, and other enterprises. They received no funds from the government-not even a sympathetic ear.

They published their ideas in an academic journal and set up a meeting for discussion in the United States. The United States government was not enthused, but engineers from France, Japan, and Germany came in large numbers. They returned home and began building prototypes and made plans for full-fledged systems using the American Ideas. They were laying out plans for the 21st century while America had no vision for the future even though the idea originated in America.

Aerospace companies faced losing government contracts as a result of defense conversion. This was in the 60s, and now in 2002, foreign countries have fast moving maglev trains moving people. America is just now getting a realistic vision. Building such systems would have served as a buffer for aerospace companies facing the loss of large weapon design contracts. Instead, many jobs were lost, technology was set back, and manufacturing plants were idled.

Complacency In Education

Dr. Powell and Dr. Danby pioneered notable inventions for the maglev trains, but the United States would not give them any money to develop their ideas in the 1960s. The ideas were something that were new to provide a fast safe quiet way of traveling on a train. It was something that was very obvious that the United States and our transportation systems needed. The train would have propelled us into the future with new jobs, but our government did not realize or even get "concerned" enough to act in a positive way. One cannot realize what effects it had on the inventors.

In the 1960s, President John F. Kennedy galvanized the nation filled with ambition and said "We are going to put a man on the moon by the end of the decade." The Apollo Program was started, congress granted the funds and engineers worked designing new products. By July of 1969, Americns had explored the moon.

This declaration was made when no one was certain about how to reach the moon, technology was not available, and there was no economic justification. The United States went forward anyway and astonished the world.

What conditioned America to lose its aggressiveness and leadership in building the maglev train? Our leaders did not use their abilities to cultivate the present for the growing future. They were not even concerned about the future. The United States had stopped analyzing the present, making decisions based on the results, and correcting them for continuous growth.

We "Became Mired In Vietnam and Lost Our Goals." Students became less concerned about being scientists and more concerned about staying out of the draft. Our school system began putting less importance on "mathematics, science, and physics." Since education is the key to technological superiority, we began losing, without even realizing it. The whole educational systems shared a part of the blame. A large part of the teachers in grade schools did not have adequate training in math or science, so students were not stimulated at an early age and failed to recognize events that could guide their thoughts.

Science teachers were being drawn into industry because of the respect and large salaries they received. In Pontiac, Michigan, a science course was taught by an Art teacher. According to the National Science Teachers Association, one third of the nation's science classes were being taught by misassigned teachers and the students received a weak background in science, mathematics, and physics. They would be deficient in those disciplines the remainder of their life.

The curriculum was a problem as well. Hands on experience has been an invaluable tool for introducing youngsters to the wonders of science. Yet nationwide, 80 percent of the seventh and eight graders never took a field trip. Fifty percent did not even have access to laboratories, and what they were taught definitely depended on where they lived. One inner-school system in Pontiac, Michigan, was so financially depressed, they could not afford any kind of science classes for its ninth grade students. Next door, the affluent Bloomfield laboratories were well equipped.

America began to be conditioned by our lax way of thinking. Our leaders did not motivate us to achieve in all ways possible. Our education deteriorated, our research and design suffered, and we were not stimulated to manufacturing our products. We were not motivated by our industry leaders, our government, or our political leaders.

Japan adopted our once great educational system, upped the intensity and launched an impressive economic assault. They turned out a uniformly well educated work force and were motivated where most or our students were turned off. The United State students really did not have much to motivate them, like President Kennedy did with his challenge to land a man on the moon.

In the early 1990s American students ranked last in advanced biology, an international study of student achievement for 17 year-olds showed. In math they also ranked last, and many American students could not handle complex science and mathematical problems. The nations' future economic growth was in jeopardy business leaders and educators warned. A report sponsored by the National Assessment of Educational Progress found serious deficiencies in the math abilities of 9 year-olds, 13 year-olds, and 17 year-olds.

Education Secretary Lauro Cavazos referred to repeated findings that United States children perform poorly in math and science. He called the situation a national tragedy, and other educators termed the survey results frightening and devastating. Albert Shanker, president of the American Federation of Teachers said, elementary school teachers will not be able to deliver unless they are required to take math and science courses to qualify for their licenses. He also added, that we have a long way to go before we turn it around.

Two-thirds of the United States students considered themselves "good at Mathematics." Only 23 percent of the highest achievers, Korean students, had that attitude. Did they really know, or were they not concerned?

The Education System

The problems were an educational system that had been teaching math and science in the same way they had taught for decades. Most schools emphasized theory and fact over practical applications and seemed more interested in testing memorization than in giving students the basis for understanding math and science for everyday use. In Burlington, VT, IBM was teaching its entire work force of 800 employees Algebra I and Algebra 11 something they should have learned in high school. The products IBM made were priced high enough to cover that cost.

The American system of public education resembled a mass-production factory that prepared the young. Students proceeded along an assembly line of sequenced grades and at each stage teachers filled their heads with standardized information. As in a mass-production line, if young students were not capable of standardized information, they fell off the production line and received no help to get back on the line. They were taught what to think, not how to think.

America had to learn to stop training the majority of our young people for jobs in which they worked like cogs in a wheel. If our future workers were to implement continuous improvement in products and processes, every student had to be educated to think critically and continually learn, based on new information. Teachers had to allow and encourage students to take more initiative in deciding what they learned and when and how they learned it.

Now in 2002, the education system has tests that different grades have to take and pass before they can graduate.

A Nobel Prize winner and professor in physics called his students scientific illiterates. However, the lack of science enthusiasm had not affected the enrollment at MIT, where most of the graduates were internationals, not Americans. Sixty percent of science degrees given in the United States went to students from foreign countries. Some stayed here and the others went back to their countries and sent us products that were better than we could produce. America's lead had slipped away.

A Manufacturing Problem

Our manufacturers were bridled and our companies failed to capitalize on good ideas. They were unwilling to take a risk as they did when the theory for the first maglev train was introduced. The Phillips Company came up with and idea of a compact disc an how to produce them. They looked for funding, but our industries thought it was too risky. A foreign country used the ideas and sales reached $1 billion dollars the first six months. The money lost was small when you consider the technology we gave away.

In the 1960s, Ampex developed radio cassette recorders, but did not recognize the potential of video products for the consumer market. Japan did. Rather than staying abreast of the world market and future potential, Ampex ignored Japan. When they decided to go after the competition it was too late. With $40 million lost, Ampex sold the company to Japan and dropped the product. In the late 1970s the products were in two-thirds of American homes. In 1987 over 12 million VCR's were imported to the United States and not one was produced in the good old USA.

The Clorox Corporation developed a laser color copying machine. The machine was 50 percent faster with better output at one half the cost of copying, and the complete machine was one-half the cost of the competitor. The company could not get any American investors willing to take a risk. With more and more paper being used every hour and with future projections, how much risk could have been involved? Clorox turned to Japan and the machine was imported from Japan with the name Sharp embedded on it.

Companies Fighting Each Other

American companies were spending large sums of money to buy out existing companies or merging to reduce competition instead of investing in the company's future. Inventions need time to grow and money to fertilize their growth, but that was spent on corporate acquisitions.

Another problem America created that caused us trouble in 2001 is research and development (R&D). Companies get their new ideas in laboratories and turn them into new technology. Corporate concerns were fighting off companies that wanted to take them over or buy them and this was taking their toll on R&D money. Borrick Warner spent two billion dollars fighting take over battles. After they won, their debt was so high that the R&D lab was the first to go.

To avoid hostile takeovers, many corporations substantially increased their ratio of debt to equity, and borrowed as much as they possibly could. They could barely make the necessary interest payments consequently, the corporations were vulnerable.

Compatible color TV was born at the David Sornof Research Center in New Jersey. When General Electric took over RCA they decided it did not need the R&D facility and sold it. The staff was cut by 300 and the research budget by 20 percent. One employee stated that they did less research than they had done 20 years ago. He also said, if we lose our research and development facilities, how can we cultivate new ideas?

We lost our "Know how" to manufacture anything. We were a nation that invented mass production during the war and it carried over to later years. Now in 2002 we have lost our technique and the technology did not keep up in manufacturing. We do not know how to make things anymore. The microchip is used to store information in computers. It was co-developed by an American, but they spent to much time developing the product. Japan was able to develop a technique to make them cheaper. The American company was forced out of the market in memory chips, even though memory chips are used in everything from cars to copiers. Getting a product to the consumer at the cheapest price is a fact that should be recognized by almost everyone.

America developed much of the technology on robots, but Japan saw the need and applied it in their automobile plants. A lot of our manufacturing plants were operating as they did years ago with the assumption that there had to be a tradeoff. Japan was operating with the knowledge that there did not have to be one.

Many of our problems were in top management because management did not know how the work was done. Unions resisted change fearing the loss of jobs with the new technology. Management were more interested in profits and not products, but profits do not produce or stimulate new ideas. The problems were like an escalator, if the present work force understood, made corrections, and build on the corrections, the next generation could stay on the escalator as it continued to move upward. Otherwise, the next generation is bumped off the escalator while it continues moving.

It would have been wise for a committee of leaders to analyze and develop a reason why we were losing products and technology when we developed it. In 2002, we have many foreign countries making products to sell in this country based on our technology. Are we giving technology away just to make money? We are paying workers to learn our secrets, and we are paying large sums of money to foreign countries as venture capital for help in building the maglev train two American's invented. We call it, "joint venture" and we find many ways to justify it.

Corning Glass spent twenty years and $200 million in R&D in optic fiber. It was a key component to telecommunications. Corning licensed that technology to Japan for sale in Japan, but not in the United States. Japan made sales in the United States anyway infringing on Corning patents. Corning sued only to learn there were clearly no established legal protections against foreign technology piracy. It took several years and millions of dollars in legal fees before Corning managed to secure its patents. They had lost the technology. They were losing $40 to $60 billion a year because America and other countries did not enforce our property rights.

In the 1940s, Mr Tucker developed a nice looking advanced car and set up to manufacture it after renting a building. The auto manufacturers and banks stopped the money and material for building the car. His cars were faster than the present vehicles and the headlights turned with the steering wheel. The vehicle manufacturers showed their narrow selfish thinking. Instead of using that car for competition to produce a better car for the public, they only thought of their benefits. Mr. Tucker was so discouraged he moved to Paris where he died.

I mentioned the above to help the reader understand America's conditioning to a loss of leadership, and some of America's failures to act. The properties for the maglev train was invented in this country in the late 1960s, but the American government failed to fund the program to develop the inventors ideas. This is very difficult to believe when you look at the following:

1. The number of vehicles sold per year
2. The constant increase in population
3. Urban growth
4. Crowded freeways
5. Lost productive time
6. Crowded airways
7. Crowded airlines
8. Airline delays
9. Transportation problems
10. Future projections
11. Congestion cost
12. Peak travel time
13. Delays
14. Wasted fuel

America has generated a new phrase, "make studies." Then they want to "make studies" of the studies, spending many dollars and losing more time. They do not realize some kind of manufacturing has to be undertaken before any progress can be made and keep building on that to get an end product. Studies are only studies and built on theories developed by the people during the studies. They should only be used in primary analysis.

America Awakens

As foreign countries started building new steel-wheel and maglev trains, was America saturated with Life, Liberty, and the pursuit of Competitiveness? Those who worried about competitiveness said, there were hard choices ahead, but it was precisely the hard choices that were being avoided. Time and again in American history when troubling public issues presented themselves, our leaders talked in abstractions about growth, progress, productivity, and competitiveness. Competitiveness is derived from actions, principles, products, and desirable human qualities. Those that should have been working to develop the next generation of transportation methods would have done well to focus on their technical virtuosity to satisfy real present and future needs.

America continues their love affair with the automobile and relies almost solely on airlines to travel. Moving large numbers of people between relatively close metropolitan areas is a problem since we cannot continue paving over America forever and sitting in traffic going nowhere fast.

Now that America realizes the maglev and steel-wheel trains are a necessity and America is over thirty years behind, it is trying to keep from spending money duplicating what has been done. However, the real reason is trying to get proven benefits from the trains that have been built, and improving on them. This effort will cost less money, save time, produce a better train, and to make it sound better, America calls it "Joint Venture."

Magnetic levitation or maglev trains are quiet, smooth, fast, and cost effective with no engine noise because they have no engines. At a train station, the maglev train stands on rubber tires. As it moves forward and reaches a speed of 25 mph, there is no physical contact with anything and the train suffers no friction except wind resistance. To correct the magnets for the guideway, the lifting currents must continually adjust fast-acting control systems to keep the train up over the guideway and will help in something like an earthquake.

Suspending objects with no visible support is fascinating and seems impossible to most people even if we can send men to space in this high-tech world. To levitate or see something as heavy as a train suspended in air seems impossible. Levitation is defined as the stable equilibrium of a body without contact with any physical thing. The forces can be created by both electric or magnetic fields. It requires two subsystems, a system for shaping or trappings the magnetic flux and a primary system for generating the magnetic field.

When we were young in age, if we put two magnets together in a certain way they "attracted" and stuck together. When they were reversed, they repulsed each other with an effort to push them apart making it difficult to push together. Large electrical powered magnets with the same forces multiplied many times together and harnessed, will generate waves strong enough to move and lift a train, called a malev train.

There are two principal methods for magnetically levitating trains. The first is called electromagnet levitation, (EML), or attracting levitation, using non-superconducting electromagnets which suspend the vehicle below ferromagnetic rails. The electromagnetic system is shown in figure 8.1.

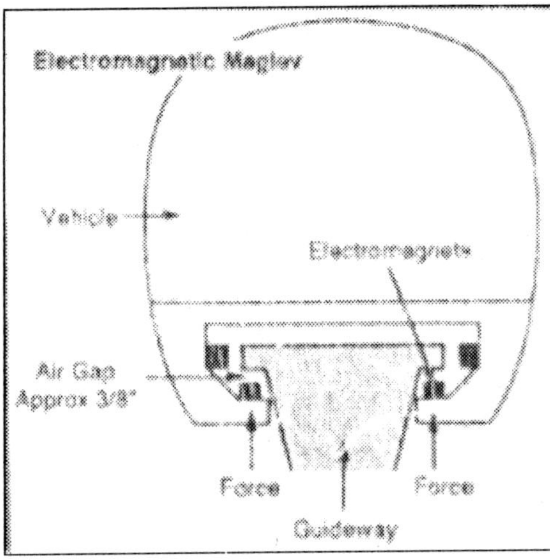

Fig. 8.1. Electromagnetic Maglev. Courtesy Federal Railroad Administration.

Electric currents in a wire-wound coil produce the primary field while the ferromagnetic (a substance with a normally high permeability) coil holder and the ferromagnetic base create a means of shaping a magnetic circuit. In the case of eddy current levitation with a moving magnet over a conductor, the source of the field can be a magnet or a normal superconducting wire wound coil.

Another explanation is, the lower part of the train has a wrap-around section on both sides with electromagnets located on the under side of each guideway over the wrap-around section. The electromagnets attract the wrap-around and as the train move forward it is attracted upward and it floats about three-eighth of an inch above the top of the guideway.

The second method is called electrodynamics levitation (EDL) or repulsive levitation, and uses large superconducting magnets on the train which generate eddy currents (an electric current induced by an alternating magnetic field) in a conducting track below the train. Lift is developed when the vehicle moves. Electromagnet is a core of magnetic material surrounded by a coil of wire that a current passed through to magnetize the core. The magnetic levitation fields suspend, guide, and propel noncontacting trains above the guideway.

The guideway is the physical structure along which the vehicle is levitated.

Electromagnets use the properties of magnets of the same polarity to repel each other and lift or push the train off rubber wheels that support the train when standing. Electromagnets on each side of the train and the magnets on the track elevate the train with minimal power and no friction. This type shown in figure 8.2 was designed by the Japanese Railways.

A shorter explanation, the magnets are located on the upper top of the guideway under the train. The upper superconducting magnets are on the botton of the train above the guideway. The magnets repulse and pushes the train up about 6 inches.

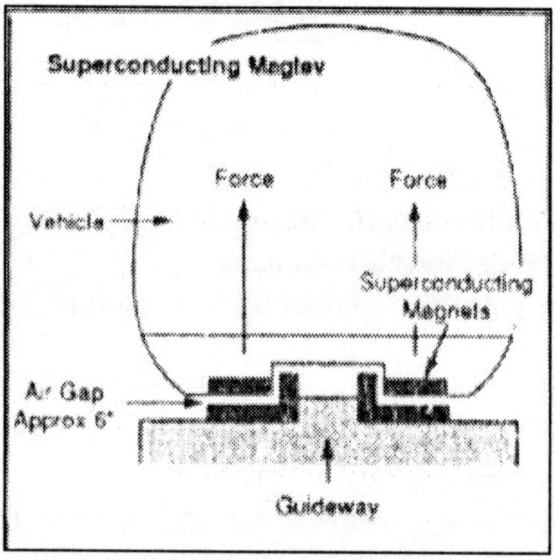

Fig. 8.2. Electrodynamic Maglev. Courtesy Federal Railroad Administration.

Other Designs

A technology was developed for the Star Wars program back in the 80s. The system was developed at the Sandia National Laboratories in Albuquerque, NM known as Segmented Rail Phase Induction Motor (SERAPHIM) that let magnetic levitation trains use existing tracks for lower-speed passenger and freight trains. Maglev trains that traveled 300 mph required dedicated and specialized tracks at a high cost. This method would save a lot of money and time by sharing the existing tracks with passenger and freight trains.

This concept has approximately 30 pairs of closely spaced electromagnetic coils attached to the lower portion of the train shown in figure 8.3. Pairs of coils straddle an added third rail that is located beneath the center part of the train or it could be adjacent to one of the normal rails. Aluminum plates are pre-assembled and bolted to the added rail like rungs on a ladder.

Seraphim, rolls on rails powered by magnetic coils.

(Fig. 8.3.)

Magnetic fields are created by a pulsed current that flows through the coils and the pulsing induces surface currents in the aluminum plates that repels the coil pushing the train down the track. Optical sensors are used so that the coil is located precisely with respect to the plate permitting the coils to be pulsed just as they pass the midpoint of each plate. A gas generator aboard the train produce power for the magnetic coils. In other maglev systems, stationary electromagnetic coils must be powered along the total length of the track causing a greater expense.

Barry Marder estimated the cost would be reduced about one-quarter to construct a SERAPHIM type high-speed rail system compared to another type of maglev system. Analyst say the investment should be recoverable in five to ten years along the most populated corridors. He also said, airlines should be included as partners rather than adversaries for a new method of transportation. The high-speed trains could be an extension up to a distance of 300 miles from where the flights end. Short flights for the airlines are highest in cost pushed by landing and taking off.

Speeds over 200 mph would require a new track to be laid instead of one rail and it would have to be machined to very tight tolerances. The other problem for 200 mph speeds or over is ordinary freight trains could not run on the line without wrecking the precision. How long would the prolonged usage last and at what speeds would the damage begin to occur?

Dr Richard Post of the Lawrence Livermore National Laboratory in California had a design called "Inducetrak" that appeared to overcome problems created with the magnetic levitation systems. Permanent magnets are not strong enough to lift a train off the track so electromagnets were used. Permanent magnet's maximum strength is dictated by the material it is made from, but the electromagnet's strength depends on the current passing through it. If more strength is needed in the electromagnet, increase the current.

The track had a group of closely-packed rectangular metal frames sequenced and each acted as a separate independent electrical circuit. As the magnets on the train pass over a frame, an electric current was induced in it. This generated a magnetic field which repelled the magnet that started the process of levitating the train.

The system used low temperature cooling systems rather than superconducting coils, which were inexpensive to operate. It consisted of unpowered passive magnet arrays attached under the train over a track guideway with nonmagnetic inductive coils embedded in its surface. When motors on the train started the train from a stationery position reaching a slow speed, the magnets and inductive coils repelled each other and the train began to float on air. The track functioned like a linear motor from energized coils.

Physicist Klaus Halbach pioneered a way to levitate a train from arrays used in particle accelerators. Efficient arrays of permanent magnet materials concentrate the magnetic field on one face of the array while nearly canceling it on the opposite side. When mounted on the bottom of the rail and a train pass over passive coils on a rail track, the Halbach arrays generate periodically varying magnetic fields that "induces" current in the closely packed track circuits. The Halback arrays on the bottom of the rail vehicles provide levitation and one on each side create lateral stability.

Another advantage is that the magnetic fields are concentrated at the lower surface of the magnets, with nearly zero magnetism above the magnets. Passengers are completely safe from magnetic fields. On maglev trains that have superconducting coils, passengers have to be shielded from the magnetic field.

Underground Maglev Systems

A new underground transportation system is planned by the Swiss government. It is a maglev train based on German Transrapid maglev technology and is called SWISSMETRO. A Swiss engineer, Rodolphe Nieth, conceived the idea in 1974. The driving force was the surrounding mountainous terrain with rugged hills with a dense population and little usable space left to expand its transport system. The residents also had a great concern for the environment and a desire to preserve their colorful towns and villages. Thus it was nearly impossible to build new roads and railways. The only answer was to go underground with the new transportation system linking principal cities and regions.

It will have two stacked tubes, each approximately 16 feet in diameter, with the top tube being buried approximately 98 feet below the surface. The train will be 11 feet in diameter leaving a clearance of 5 feet which will lower the construction costs. It will also generate the problems that prevents it being cost effective. See figure 8.4 for two stacked tunnels, walkways, and a train station.

Fig. 8.4. Swiss underground two train tunnels and station. Courtesy Eurotunnel.

Since the tube diameter is not much bigger than the vehicle, the forward movement of the vehicle will cause air to accumulate in front of the train, creating air resistance as the train moves forward. The air resistance will increase with speed, requiring more energy to propel the vehicles.

Normally, to eliminate the sound barrier problem that limits the airflow around the sides of the train and sets up a rising pressure wave in front of the vehicle, tunnels are usually bored with much bigger diameters than the vehicle. Another problem encountered will be the vacuum created in the tunnels which will require pressurized vehicles like the airplane cabins. What would be some of the problems created if malfunctions occur?

Using space on the lower portion of the tubes would not leave much room on the sides or the top underneath the surface. Thus at speeds of 200 mph, the pressures and sound barrier should be tremendous.

The Swiss government's plan for the system is a long train. It will have a capacity for 800 passengers and is planned for a travel time of 12 minutes between stations and have four or even eight trains per hour. Cost estimates for 200 miles is $10 billion and the entire system is estimated to be $21 billion. It is expected to be operational by 2020.

In 1802, Napoleon liked a proposal from Albert Mathieu a mining engineer in France, for a tunnel. In 1986, after many wars, French President Francois Mitterrand and British Prime Minister Margaret Thatcher agreed to permit a rail system to be built in a tunnel for trains under the English Channel that linked Britain and France. The time between Paris and London was reduced to 3 hours, less than the usual 7 & 1/2 hours.

The Eurotunnel opened economic benefits to other countries, with one of the contributing factors shorter travel times. It consists of, 24 miles under the sea and 12 miles overland. As shown in figure 8.5, it has two single track tunnels for the trains and in the middle of the two is a smaller tunnel for servicing, ventilation, and maintenance.

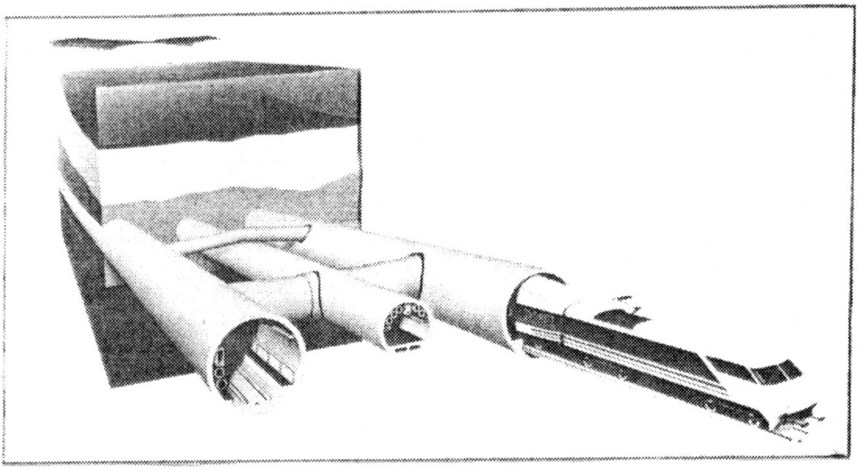

Fig. 8.5. A Eurotunnel under the sea with two rail tunnels and a service tunnel for servicing, maintenance, and ventilation. Courtesy Eurotunnel.

Propulsion and Super-conductivity

Japan built a test track west of Tokyo. They were able to run trains at design speeds on curves, slopes, in tunnels, and past trains going the opposite direction. The 27-mile test track was long enough for full-size cars to travel at 310 mph for three minutes. Previously propulsion coils had been placed in a single layer in the side walls of the guideway. They were set edge to edge and there was a discontinuity that caused the superconducting electromagnets on the cars to heat up. They were later placed in two staggered layers with no interruption in the magnets.

Later figure eight shaped coils were mounted on the side walls of the guideway in front of the propulsion coils. When the center of the on-board superconducting coil was not aligned with the center of the figure eight, it induced a current in the guideway coils that generated magnetic forces tending to pull the centers into alignment moving the train forward. Those magnetic forces also levitated the train.

Super-conductivity refers to the ability of a material to carry electricity without electrical resistance near absolute zero (a hypothetical temperature characterized by complete absent of heat and equivalent to approximately -273.15* C or -495.67* F). It can help the maglev systems by reducing the amounts of electrical power needed to operate properly, reduces the weight of magnets aboard the vehicles, and cuts cost to build weight saving guideways. The superconducting magnets lift the vehicle to within a fraction of an inch of a rail guide. Keeping the train airborne and in motion requires accurate feedback circuits and very high tolerances.

Another type takes superconducting coils and runs their magnetic field past a conductive plate to achieve levitation force.

Early guideways had various configurations, U-shaped, Y-shaped, T-shaped, Aluminum, concrete, and box-beams made of steel.

Linear electric motors built into the guideway generate a traveling magnetic field that pulls the train along or an inboard motor that induces propulsion forces in a metal guideway plate. This technology enables maglev trains to easily attain very high speeds at distances of 300 miles or more. For distances of 300 miles they are faster than air travel adding time to the airport, park, boarding times, and delays or cancellation that is well known now.

As speed increases the magnetic drag force decreases in eddy-current-repulsion-based systems and aerodynamic forces increase dramatically. Aerodynamic forces on moving vehicles close to the ground plane are usually divided into two parts: form drag and skin drag. The form drag is proportional to the frontal areas whereas the skin drag is proportional to the vehicle length, cross-sectional perimeter, and the viscosity of air.

The analogous of form drag is moving a flat plate in air normal to its frontal area. Ideally, the flow should move from the front face to the back face with no drag at all. In reality, the flow separates in the form of viscous eddies, resulting in a higher fluid pressure on the front of the object and a lower pressure on the back.

Some of the engineering and operational issues in Maglev designs are listed.

1. Maintenance
2. Switching
3. Route selection
4. Ride quality
5. Cost
6. Noise
7. Headway, capacity
8. Magnetic field in cabin
9. Communication and control
10. Curve negotiation, tilting, grade climbing ability
11. Magnet design, cryogenics, helium management
12. Emergency operation: egress, fire, loss of magnet
13. Guideway repair and inspection
14. Power, substations, utility interface
15. Station-guideway compatibility

Time to Act

The US had the talent and technology to propel the US into the future as a competitor, but this country's leadership tended to react to the present rather than continually planning for the future. Like the proverbial ostrich with his head in the sand, and even with its long neck when erected, could not see over the hill.

The Department of Transportation followed a request from Congress, and submitted a preliminary report on the economic and technical reasons for designing a maglev multitrack systems that could also operate in tunnels.

The US Army Corps of Engineers followed a directive from Congress to submit a preliminary plan for the development. It also concluded that maglev routes could be made and the maglev could run for a profit. In April 1990, the Department of Transportation and other agencies formed the National Maglev Initiative to coordinate, conduct research, and evaluate a maglev system. They wanted to evaluate maglev's potential for determining a successful way for the Federal Government to improve transportation in the inner-city.

In December 1991, the Interrmodal Surface Transportation Efficiency Act authorized $725 million for a maglev prototype development program, but no funding was appropriated for fiscal years 1992 or 1993. It was to be a five year plan to build a 20 mile prototype system. In the spring of 1992, Bush senior reversed his decision, Congress went along, and the effort was halted. In the fiscal year of 1993, $9.8 million was appropriated to complete the study at high priority.

The National Initiative asked for proposals through the Broad Agency Announcement, but out of 250 responses, 27 were awarded $4.4 million dollars to design a maglev system.

Some of the things they were interested in:

1. Noise for high-speed rail and maglev systems.
2. Guideway sensor systems.
3. Guideway structure.
4. Maglev route alignment and right-of-way.
5. Aerodynamic forces on maglev vehicles.
7. Suspension and propulsion.
8. Application of cable-in-conduit.
9. Power distribution.
10. Power transfer speed.
11. Analysis of magnetic fields.

6. Safe speed enforcement.
12. Wayside control and communication.

The Maglev Initiative later awarded four systems totaling $8.6 million. The propulsion, braking, suspension, controls, vehicle, and guideway were to be analyzed. The designs were to consider cost, safety, design detail, and performance to determined if there were merits for a 300 mph maglev in the United States.

The United States Department of Transportation could underwrite more than one prototype high-speed magnetic train as a way of testing different types of systems. Five designs and cost were considered to be evaluated and a cost determined:

1. The cost of elevated guideways in the millions of dollars per mile for two, one steel-wheel train and one maglev train.
2. Cost of grade guideways.
3. Range of initial capital cost.
4. Maximum percent of grade incline.
5. Acceleration times with full thrusts, 0-186 mph and 0-300 mph.

They Wanted to:

1. Acquire maglev technology developed in Germany and Japan since they already had the know how.
2. Undertake advanced maglev development in partnership with Germany or Japan.
3. Invest in an advanced United States maglev system or high-speed rail comparable to alternatives using existing maglev technology.

Table 8.1 list the parameters.

Table 8.1

Parameter of Trains Listed
($22.30 represents $22,300,000)

Parameter	TGV Steel Wheel	TRO7 Maglev	US Maglev
Elevated Guideway	$22.30	$16.60	$17.60
At Grade Guideway	$3.30	$17.40	$17.60
Range of Initial Capital Cost Millions per Mile	$17.20 to $33.40	$30.40 to $49.30	$26.60 to $45.40
Cruise Speed, mph	200	311	300
Percent Maximum Grade	5%	10%	30%
Acceleration time, Full Thrust			
in Minutes 0.186	6.80	1.78	0.50
0.300	0.80	4.10	0.90
Total Bank Angle in Degrees	7	12	30

Source: Final Report on the National Maglev Initiative

A high-speed transportation system had strong support in the United States. The responses of the private and academia sector during the National Maglev Initiative program demonstrated both the interest and capability to initiate a United States design system. A design system would better serve the characteristic of the United States Market. Some of the things they were interested in was greater distances between major cities, operational demand for airline-quality service, and consumers demanding higher levels of inner-city service.

The delay of the United States getting in the maglev form of transportation was considered an advantage. The United States could build on the present designs that had been used and been effective. They could also take the best of their designs and build on it, since the technology has moved ahead and some of the new designs would have spin-offs that could be used to manufacture other material. There is always a form of paradox that accompanies difference approaches. The United States also hoped to increase interest in foreign countries when the products were completed. The new designs would also created more jobs in the United States.

Considering the relative immaturity of current American markets and the long lead time necessary to design and construct a system, private industry was unlikely to have the incentive to develop that technology on its own. Inter-governmental cooperation would be necessary to help coordinate and possibly fund a private sector whose internal priorities would supersede any national commitment. In view of potential benefits of experience gained by joint ventures with foreign partners, there would appear to be very little to lose in joint venture participation in design competition, if a substantial share of the development was guaranteed to take place in the United States.

Based on knowledge from Germany and Japan, the National Maglev Initiative said, maglev transportation would be a convenient alternative for travelers between large urban areas. It would share with the airline delays and highway congestion by carrying passengers for short trips. Technology would be advanced and less oil or petroleum would be used. The agency concluded that the new system would provide benefits for businesses in the United States work force, and develop new technology coordinating with foreign countries.

Joint Venture

The joint venture could be characterized as cooperative efforts between foreign and American firms for introducing maglev systems into the United States. It could take the form of government-to-government ventures given to industry or some combination of advanced designs and a shared development program. Germany and France were the only countries with good running prototype systems, and the United States could use them as a model. The joint venture process would use either the Japanese steel-wheel system or German maglev system or both as a baseline and then improve on it with

United States industry participation. Some things both partners could benefit from.

Reduced Development Cost

Relying on existing maglev systems developed abroad also had the advantage of lower development costs. It had significant disadvantages of older technology that was not designed for United States markets, but joint ventures had advantages. It would enable programs to benefit from experiences of established efforts. To benefit fully from recent maglev development abroad, joint ventures between United States companies and foreign companies should be permitted to develop activities substantial in the United States. Because of the over $800 million and financial risks of such a program, it would require that there be a form of milestone check that would help in the continued revaluation. There were two serious practical issues, who does the work and who pays for it?

The French TGV (*trains a grande vitesse)* operated moving people at the International Traffic Fair in Hamburg, Germany. It operated over 12 years, carrying a quarter of a billion passengers. There has never been a passenger fatality on the grade-separated French high-speed line so it is possible to reduce the probability of collisions above an acceptable level. It is a steel-wheel train that roll on rails like conventional trains, but uses powerful electric motors, better suspension systems, computerized signaling and lighter and more aerodynamic cars for safety and comfort. Speeds of 170 to 210 mph were typical for commercial service.

The German maglev initiative developed the TR07 shown in figure, 8.6 at a cost of over $1 billion and used separate conventional iron-core attracting electromagnets to generate vehicle lift and guidance.

Fig. 8.6. Maglev Transrapid TR07. Courtesy Transrapid International

Developing improvements to the German Transrapid TR07 system was to meet United States specifications. It was to have better acceleration/deceleration and vehicle tilt capability that would require significant efforts and funding. Because of limited redevelopment time and costs, the developer would prefer to perform the necessary redesigns and testing with the experienced staff in Germany. It was highly unlikely in the short run that the joint venture partners would fund and build facilities in the United States that duplicated those in Germany.

To get help on designing a maglev train, was to acquire maglev technology currently being developed. Also as a second choice, to undertake advanced maglev development partnership with two countries. Another option was to invest in an advanced United States Maglev development program. It would offer economic goals and jobs. The estimated cost for building the systems was, \$27 million to \$46 million per mile, and those prices included what degree of urbanization used, preparation, and terrain.

The Attracting Maglev

In 1997, the National Magnetic Initiatives decided to concentrate on the attraction maglev system with linear induction motors for propulsion and wayside power connection to the linear synchronized motors.

The Transrapid TR07 was developed by a German consortium. It is attracted upward toward a guideway by on-board magnets powered by batteries for extra safety. Coils along the guideway propel the vehicle and computers in the engineer's cabin communicate with controls along the train's path.

It used a linear induction motor propulsion system with wayside power collection to the linear synchronous motors. The long-stator motor for propulsion and central controlled wayside stations provided the requisite variable frequency, variable voltage power, and was designed to cruise at 311 mph.

Maglev Right-of-way

There is enough clearance for rural interstates right-of-ways for maglev construction along the median or sides of the existing right-of-ways as seen in figure 8.7.

The maglev guideway will encounter many overpasses and interchanges along vehicle routes. Since it will not be acceptable to relocate or modify most of the bridges and ramps on the intestates, it may be necessary to elevate the maglev guideway to a height allowing it to pass over existing structure and it could run alongside the interstate or in the median. The other alternative would be to run the guideway at grade level passing under existing bridges where possible. This would be suitable only in rural areas where the medians are wider.

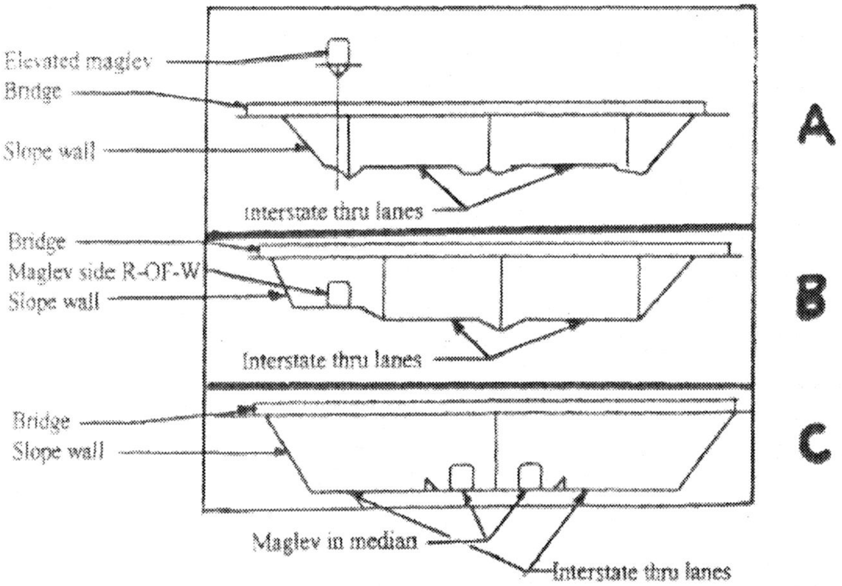

Fig. 8.7. Maglev systems along intestates. Courtesy: Andrew Anderson

This system concept would allow maglev trains to make use of electronic switches and turnouts. These switches have no moving parts and can substantially reduce the cost of achieving the tolerances required for rapid levitation. This will lead to higher train speeds through switches, reduced headway trip time, and increase system capacity.

The vehicle is wrapped around a T-shaped guideway of steel or concrete beams constructed and erected to very tight tolerances. It has a control system that regulate levitation and guidance forces to maintain approximately 3/8 of an inch between the bottom of the train and the guideway. Attraction between vehicle magnets and edge-mounted guideway rails provide guidance. The addition is between a second set of magnets and the propulsion stator packed underneath the guideway generating lift. The lift magnets also served as the secondary or motor whose primary or stator is an electrical winding running the length of the guideway. Centrally controlled wayside stations provide the requested variable-frequency and variable-voltage.

Several innovations surfaced as a result of the system concept definition work. The high power, efficient propulsion system, and a 30 degree tilt capability would allow maglev to negotiate existing railroads. The total petroleum savings, over 16 corridors for the year 2020 are estimated to be 21 million barrels for the German TR07 maglev and 15 million barrels for the steel-wheel TGV.

The diversion of interstate trips from air and auto to rail modes and maglev train results in net reductions in energy usage, petroleum consumption, emissions of most airborne pollutants, and loved ones lost in accidents. The words might carry more weight if each person said, my life might be saved by riding the train.

In developing a maglev system, it is viewed as a part of broader plans for United States economic development, and it is in this context that its national impact is relevant. The economic goals of job creation, technological advancement, and international competitiveness would be enhanced by the development and building of maglev systems on existing right-of-ways or new right-of-ways for increased speeds. When that is the preferred option, it can also reach much higher average speeds than are possible with the existing German or Japanese systems.

Maglev Right-Of-Way Cost

The guideway costs are about half of the initial construction cost of trains, ancillary facilities, civil reconstruction, and stations. The initial capital cost of the system is the most dominant and ranges from \$5.7 billion to \$21.4 billion based on urban construction and distances. Construction cost per mile of a rail system in an urban area is a much lower cost. Life cycle cost for a Guideways drives the major costs.

The two systems use different equipment between the transmission lines and the guideway. One system proposed locating each coil in the guideway. That required thousands of high-power solid state power control devices for the performance. This method and others that were proposed presented opportunities for other similar systems. Even though the maglev would be floating on air, magnets also have to be able to accept vibration.

Other designs had been used for systems that were not using liquid helium for a refrigerant. Increased power efficiency of the cryogenic system caused no resistance for electrical currents. A new approach because other countries were putting efforts in the development of high temperatures. Superconductor power through turns might be required when following existing United States right-of-ways near highways and on existing railroads. It would also support deceleration and bank angles when rounding curves.

The United States had other concerns for a maglev system. Land is costly or unavailable for highway use, but existing right-of-ways could be acceptable for the train. A new system could be designed with new composite materials and innovative train components to reduce weight and energy consumption. The airplane manufacturers do the same, discovering products that can be used in other designs. Also promising innovations for further technological improvements could be an advantage. This would reduce the cost and improve performance of a United States maglev system using spin-offs.

The United States advances in semiconductor technology would reduce on board battery requirements associated with train weight. The new knowledge would reduce both capital, operating cost, and improve efficiencies. A study included only distances related to costs of guideway structure, electric power supply, propulsion, control systems, train costs, costs of major facilities, such as stations and maintenance control centers, land acquisition, site preparation, earth moving, tunneling or long span bridges, program management, and other contingencies.

Some other cost elements are surveying, right-of-way, preparation, fencing, access roads, traffic control, demolition, reconstruction of existing buildings, roads, utilities, and the length of the system.

New Designs

New designs would provide an opportunity to develop new technologies and industries with possible benefits for United States businesses and a work force. The work would increase the Nation's productivity in related fields, and generate both high technology and construction jobs. Potential for applications in other fields would give business further advantages. The technology development process itself would require direct and secondary jobs consisting of high technology white collar jobs.

The big cost of gradually laying track all across this country in the past took time, money, and also provided many jobs. That form of transportation lasted a number of years, but now is another time when we have to provide faster trains and elevated guideways for safety in the inter-city and inner-city travel. We have to move a lot more people that will continue to increase in larger numbers every year. What will it be like ten years from now? The suspended systems will cost more than the at-grade level systems, but will offer more safety and be cost effective, less time lost, less railroad crossing congestion, and more safety for now and the future.

The Government staff used a standard method to estimate the cost of each design in comparing the German Maglev TRO7 and the steel-wheel French TGV high-speed system.

New manufacturing techniques would be developed for the dynamic behavior and construction tolerances of concrete structures. These methods have to be used in civil construction projects for installing the system along existing highways with minimal disruption. To extend the life of concrete structures, nonconducting nonmagnetic polymer reinforcing materials would be used. The growth of fiber reinforced plastics industry could result in cost reductions and greater utilization of these materials in other applications. The materials would reduce the life cycle cost when used in the renovation of highways and bridges. The guideways could incorporate devices to assure that it was not easily damage by accidents or earthquakes.

The structural properties of a maglev guideway, such as beam rigidity and accuracy of alignment, need to be the same for all maglev systems because they derive from ride quality considerations which are the same for all passenger carrying systems. The United States Maglev is defined in terms of maximum speed, acceleration, banking capability, grade and curving capability, guideway, and relative costs. The maglev would reduce trip time that is important to making maglev competitive. This will be accomplished by providing a 30 degree banking capability, as in an airplane, and a high performance propulsion system. The additional acceleration capacity depicted for the United States maglev represents potential power to maintain 0.16gs. The additional acceleration capacity depicted for the United States maglev represents potential power to maintain 0.15gs climbing steep grades.

Maglev Noise

Even though maglev trains travel in the air, they still make noise from mechanical and structural sources, including vibrations. The sources are vehicle body vibrations and guideway vibrations. They radiate sounds at very low acoustical frequencies and their resonance frequencies are from guideway support beams and below 10 Hz. Radiation from box beam panel radiate up to 80 Hz and vibrations of the vehicle body can have sound radiation throughout the audible range.

Noise from magnets in a maglev system is a result of induced vibration from large magnetic forces. These forces are located at magnet gaps between the vehicle and the guideway, and sound radiation come from there as well as from larger structures, like vehicle panels, and guideways that cause them to vibrate in response to such forces.

Magnetic pole passing causes noise. Maglev guideway structures are subject to similar loading forces as a conventional train, leading to similar vibrations and radiated sound from the guideway. The vehicle body constructions may also be similar to conventional train cars in response to dynamic forces, resulting in similar vibration and sound radiation characteristics. See figure 8.8 for a maglev train as it passes over a farmer's pasture with animals feeding.

Fig 8.8. Maglev quiet run across a farmers pasture. Courtesy Transrapid International.

Frequency sources:

1. Line frequencies.
2. Guideway-span crossing frequencies and harmonics.
3. Stator-pole passing frequencies high in electric magnet levitation, lower in eletrodyamic levitation.
4. A single frequency source can create a wide spectrum of frequencies
5. Harmonics and sub-harmonics.

Aerodynamic noise can be generated the same as on a steel-wheel train, at the nose and rear sections of the train, along the train surface, and between the train-guideway gap as noted:

1. Air flow past edges
2. Flow over cavity resonance's
3. Turbulent boundary layer along the body surface
4. Separation of flow and reattachment.

This suggest that the way guideway coils are attached to the structure may affect the radiated aeroacoustic noise. Acceptance of the new transportation system may depend on human environmental effects such as noise.

At 248 mph the German built maglev TR07 appears to be 7 dB quieter than the steel-wheel TGV. When the speeds approach 310 mph the gap seems to disappear. See table 8.2.

Table 8.2

Comparison of Noise Characteristies of Transportation and other Activities

Vehicle	DB Sound Level
Wishpering	30
Light auto traffic at 100 ft	50
Conversational speech	60
Vacuum cleaner at 10 ft	69
Freight train at 50 ft	75
Shinkansen at 150 mph at 83 ft	**80**
Alarm clock at 2 ft	80
Riding inside a city bus	83
Transrapid at 185 mph at 82 ft	**84**
Heavy truck at 50 ft	90
TGV at 185 mph at 82 ft	**91**
Jet take off at 2000 ft	105
Jet take off at 200 ft	120
Threshold of physical pain	130

Source: Office of Technology Assessment, 1991, based on US General Accounting Office data.

Maglev Is Safe

One environmental worry about Supertrains is they are powered by electricity and could increase demands on power plants. Increased electrical usage does not mean more pollution. High-speed trains use electrical power, and they would reduce the demand for less acceptable types of energy consumption, gasoline in vehicles, and kerosene in jet airplanes. Since 1973, electrical companies have reduced emissions by 21 percent, even through the use of coal to generate electricity has jumped by 88 percent and they are employing new technologies that will increase efficiency and reduce pollution even more.

Starting Supertrain service in North America is a political problem, the technological problems have been solved. Congressmen have trouble imagining the possibilities because so few of them know anything about Supertrains. Companies in New York, Pennsylvania, Vermont, and Texas, however, want to built the trains for the United States and sell them to foreign countries.

Maglev trains in open country could cruise at 300 mph, but speeds would be lower in urban areas. Curves on urban interstates are tighter, rights-of-ways are narrower, and the surrounding areas built up, reducing the maglev speed between approximately 100 to 150 mph. In certain cities, stations will be relatively close together, requiring slower speeds, but it is not necessary for maglev vehicles to stop at every station in urban regions, the Argonne report said. "By using off-line loading, maglev trains will be able to stop at selected stations and bypass others."

Should the ground shudder in an earthquake, the line would be protected the same way the Japanese safe guard their Bullet Trains. Seismometers are installed at substations every 12 miles along the line, and are also placed every 50 miles in other locations. The systems alerts a central control system and trains are stopped automatically during earthquakes. The network is so sophisticated that it transmits information by satellite when land cables are damaged by large ground movements. The Bullet Trains have been protected for over 25 years from Japan's frequent earthquakes.

Another fear is that the magnetic waves (EMF) from the train or the guideway will harm passengers or neighbors along the line. The magnetic leakage from the guideway to surrounding areas is considerably less than from electromagnetic fields associated with overhead power lines. The major reason, magnetic fields are generated when the current changes rapidly. The maglev guideway is energized only at the moment when a train is passing.

Canadian Institute of Guided Ground Transport Researchers examined a German system. They found the Transrapid vehicle would not generate magnetic fields strong enough to harm either human beings or sensitive equipment such as wristwatches or heart pacemakers. The magnetic field is far below that found in electric blankets.

Maglev Advantages

One of the things learned is that in many cities, existing bridges, tunnels, and transportation corridors are not being used to full capacity and could be inexpensively modified to accommodate maglev. Techniques exist for coupling maglev trains or mounting them on rail to provide near term access to rail terminals. Maglev facilities would be built in congested areas and larger air gaps would enhance the safety of the system by increasing the tolerance to design irregularities arising from damage, earthquakes, or improper maintenance as a safety factor.

A potential exists in the United States for using high-speed trains in high density corridors as an alternative to existing inter-city transportation modes such as air or auto. There are four basic options dictating different roles and responsibilities for both the Federal Government, the private sector, different technology, and economic impacts.

Trains are a good opposite for airport expansion because airplane runways consume large amounts of land and trains use relatively little land. Some advantages:

1. Electrically powered, they reduce petroleum dependence in comparison with air and auto.
2. Acceleration/breaking permits speeds over four times the highway speed limit of 65 mph posted speeds, reduced to 35 mph.
3. A capacity of a least 12,000 passengers per hour in each direction with potential for even higher capacities of 3 to 4

minute headway. It can support traffic growth in the twenty-first century and beyond and prove an alternative to air and auto in the event of an oil availability crisis.

4. Less susceptible to congestion and weather conditions than air or highway giving high reliability. Variance from schedule can average less than one minute.
5. A larger amount of comfort compared to air travel, with no air turbulence ensuring a consistently smooth and quiet ride with automatic doors between cars and freedom and stability to move around.
6. High speed and safety.
7. High frequency service and the ability to serve central business districts, airports, and other major metropolitan area nodes.
8. Passengers diverted to maglev from air travel reduce demand and congestion at airports, which is large congestion relief benefits for many cities and corridors.
9. A net reductions in injuries and fatalities because of diversions from auto traffic.

Dr. Powell wanted a National Maglev Network similar to the interstate highway systems stretching through 42 states with a maximum speed of 300 mph. It would cost in the billions, but Powell says that's less than a quarter of what the US spends on current transportation systems each year. The government could recoup its investment in a short time, providing an efficient mode of travel that can keep expanding at a small cost.

This could be equated to building the early railroad systems. Expanding the existing systems for high speeds and comforts with a better safety record than "any other" mode of transportation. It is the only form of transportation that can be used that is cost effective. Everything subconsciously guides America to this conclusion as more people travel, population continues to grow, uncertain petroleum supplies, and more strains on our health.

New Employment

The Northeast Corridor was selected as an example of the numbers and types of jobs to be expected. Construction of an operational maglev systems extending from Washington, DC to Boston would require large amounts of labor and construction would also be in Florida, Texas and other states. A part of that labor would be required to produce the material and purchased parts passed through in the costs. Employees would be required to operate, maintain the system, and provide services for the passengers. This would create jobs while employment is down.

These would be new jobs rather than shifts from other economic activities depending on whether the economy is operating at full employment and on how the development and implementation is financed.

This new transportation mode is technically and economically sound. Maglev development can also be viewed as a part of a broader plan for United States economic development, and it is in this context that its national impacts are relevant. Economic goals of job creation, technological advancement, and international competitiveness would be enhanced by the development and building of maglev systems.

Looking ten years into the future, based on present and pass modes of transportation, what will be a better way to move large bodies of people on long or short trips. The millions of dollars spent for just keeping the airports in operation will not solve the present and future problems.

Evaluating and comparing three modes of transportation ten years from now by airplanes, vehicles, or high speed trains are listed:

1. One rail mile for a high speed train is equivalent to one mile for ten lanes of highway with a tremendous saving in cost of real estate, congestion, petroleum, and health.
2. Cost of right-of-way for trains vs cost of a new wide right-of-ways for a highway or new airport runways.

3. One train carrying 300 passengers is equivalent to 300 vehicles.
4. Future traffic supported economically by increasing the number of train cars and adding new schedules. No increasing winglock or gridlock. Continuous cost effective transportation into the future.
5. With growing numbers of travelers, more trains on tracks vs more cancellation, waiting, winglock or gridlock.
6. Reduced railroad repair using ballast and concrete ties. Reduced repair of guideways vs repair of highways and runways.
7. Lower cost of maintaining train stations vs airport, airport accessories, and roadways.
8. Increase in productive time.
9. No cancellations or delays for overbooking. No weather delays.
10. Shorter trip time.
11. Good acceleration/deceleration and no reduced speed on hills. Good for carrying freight.

Maglevs Floating In America

The Argonne Laboratory report issued in June 1989, found that 300 mph maglev Supertrains could help alleviate growing aviation gridlock, winglock, cancellation, and overbooking by serving busy airports. Mr. Fritz Plous said, diverting from air to rail on most of the passenger trips of less than 300 miles and a substantial number of trips in the 400-mile range would provide much needed help. Such short-distance travel represents more than 25 percent of the trips handled to and from O'Hare in Chicago. See figure 8.9 for the average number of short distance flights for ten busy airports in 1989.

Miles x ten

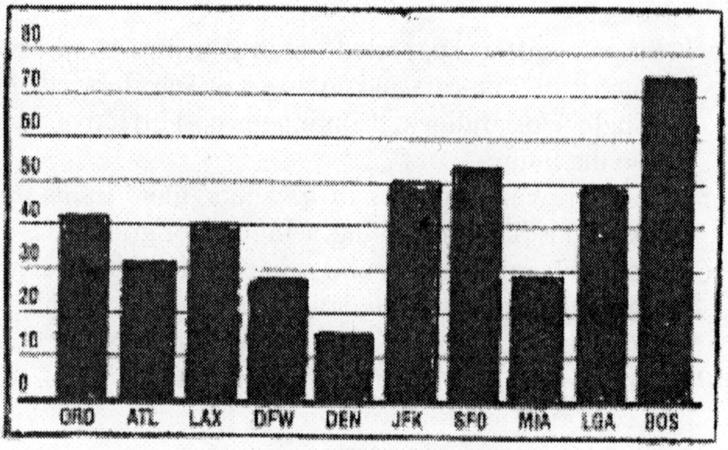

Airlines

Fig. 8.9. One month percent of short distance flights for ten busy airports in 1989. Courtesy Official Airline Guide.

Short trips diverted from air travel have shown to be the largest source of revenue.

Trip time includes estimates for terminal egress and access time at both ends of the trip as well as time spent in terminals. On short trips, when trip time is totaled, the air mode of travel advantage over maglev is generally eliminated or reduced. The increase in time for security checks, and airline delays will only increase the trip time.

Maglev fares will compete with air fares and are lowered where the maglev travel time is larger. Maglev's trip time compared to auto modes is shorter when long distances are considered. Speed restrictions, stops, and congestion delays are used for averaging the trip time and cannot be accurately anticipated.

A maglev system networks could radiate from major airports and be built for the equivalent cost to airlines and their passengers for current air traffic delays estimated by the Federal Aviation Administration at $5 billion annually. If maglev systems were integrated into major hub airports, they would become economical in many high-density United States corridors. They should also connect downtown and major suburban developments as part of inter-city travel.

Three Systems America Should Build

America should build three types of maglev systems: metropolitan feeders, inter-city corridors vs inner-city, and multi-state networks. Feeder systems would connect outlying areas of a metropolitan with its core, starting 125 miles out, with stations approximately 15 miles apart. The big cities would use maglev feeders along the interstates.

The researchers said inter-city corridors also appear to be promising. They examined a San Francisco-Los Angeles-San Diego along busy I-5 and concluded that the route, with branches along other highways such as I-10, would serve almost all of the population of California.

The Senate report concluded that maximum benefits would result from multi-state interconnected maglev networks, such as an eastern system connecting with another in the midwest.

Building A Network

The Argon's staff recommended building a 2,000 mile, $30 billion network that would serve many of the busiest airports. By comparison, to build two aircraft carriers would cost $38 billion Senator Harry Reid of Nevada said. William Lindner of the Transportation workers Union of America in a Philadelphia speech said, "It seems to me that if we are going to be effective in hauling passengers comfortably and quickly and cheaply, we have got to provide connections that have been ignored up to now."

His views have been supported by four other rail unions, the Transportation and Communications Workers Union, which represents both airline and railroad employees, labor organizations representing the locomotive engineers, signalmen, and the maintenance-right-of-way workers. After the Argon report was issued, government studies strongly endorsed maglev networks. It was issued by an advisory committee to the Senate Committee on Environment and Public Works, chaired by Daniel Patrick Moynihan of New York.

A network of trains would provide clean fast transportation without our air being increasingly polluted in our cities destroying our environment. Trains are the technology now and the future. When ozone stings our eyes or carbon monoxide burns our lungs, it is not because a train emitted it. When petroleum runs short, is is not because a train guzzled it, and when a cloud of pollution hangs over our cities, it is not because a train pulled it there.

The Dutch environment ministry is considering banning private autos in big cities, and encourages people to use trains for trips between cities. Smog kills and estimated six people a day in Athen, Greece and that city has restricted the number of cars entering its central core.

Inter-City Trains

Texas is ready to forge ahead with France's steel-wheel TGV train and a rail system linking five of the states largest cities, Dallas, Fort Worth, Austin, Houston, and San Antonio. The rail system is slated to run directly into the Dallas-Fort Worth Airport, stopping at American Airline and Delta Airline gates so baggage can be easily unloaded and loaded between planes and trains. They plan 60 trains on the 590-mile rail line, running 18 hours a day at intervals of 15 to 30 minutes. It will match 97 percent on time performance record with France's TGV trains and will consist of first-class coaches, business coaches, and a food/bar car.

The trains would be manufactured by Bombardier with GEC Alsthoun of France supplying the major components. New dedicated tracks will be built by Morrison-Knudsen, and other partners using continuous rails and concrete ties along existing railroad right-of-ways.

The transrapid maglev train is also slated be used for the Orlando system and will be manufactured and tested in Germany, disassembled and shipped to Orlando where the cars will be reassembled. It will be a five-car train and ride on an elevated guideway carrying as many as 400 passengers and 1,000 pieces of baggage per trip making up to 32 round trips a day. It will have good acceleration/deceleration with comforts and is more easily adapted for freight duty because the lack of friction on levitating trains means there are no traction problems with heavy loads.

A projection in the year of 2010 is 6.13 million one-way riders on approximate 16,780 daily trips that will average 182 miles. Approximately 58 percent will be for business and the remaining 42 percent is expected to be in tourism. Forty-five percent of the ridership is estimated to leave their travel by auto, 31 percent is expected to shift from air travel, and 24 percent would be just because of the comfort and conveniences. Eighty percent of Florida's air traffic will be high-speed rail.

Illinois is planning for the steel-wheel and maglev systems. Chicago, being the hub, is to have a line linking Chicago with Detroit and St. Louis. A second link from Chicago linking Milwaukee, Minneapolis, and a third line linking Chicago's O'Hare airport.

Northwest states will use links from Portland, Seattle, Vancouver, Spokane to Seattle, and Spokane to Washington.

Nevada and California plan to use a system based on the transrapid TR07 linking Las Vegas and Southern California. Los Angeles is to be linked to San Diego, Los Angeles to Pamdale, Bakersfield, Sacramento, and San Francisco. One of the needs is a Los Angeles, San Diego and San Francisco link. Other routes are Los Angeles International Airport to Union Station in downtown Los Angeles to Ontario Airport and on to the former March Air Force Base in Riverside County. There are supposed to be links to Anaheim, Arcadia, and San Bernardino.

The city favors the maglev systems to link those cities and the Central Valley. A maglev system from Los Angeles to San Francisco would cost $31 billion, but could such an expenditure be justified when air travel serves the region well? Los Angeles International Airport needs to distribute commuter flights to other airports inland such as Orange County and speedy rail or maglev links could make that possible.

Los Angeles California needs a transportation systems that benefits their economies and social lives. It and other Southern California cities have not been able to do so. Tokyo, Moscow, Berlin, Paris, London, New York, San Francisco-Oakland, and scores of other cities have built public transportation systems that benefited their economies and social lives.

The California region will be competing with Florida, Pennsylvania, and Maryland for federal money to help on their maglev system. The money probably will be awarded in 2006.

Another group was developing a similar maglev commercial system for Pittsburgh and Philadelphia. It intends to build a 20 mile transrapid TR07 type system connecting downtown Pittsburgh with the new airport. The company hopes this project will be the beginning of a regional maglev system spanning Pennsylvania cities, Ohio, West Virginia, Maryland, and Washington DC. Pittsburgh is to connect to the city's airport and downtown area, using Germany's transrapid maglev trains to Washington D.C., Baltimore, Philadelphia, New York City, and Boston.

Maglev systems would be costly and high-speed steel-wheel trains can be built for less money per mile. The cost of maglev trains is frequently estimated at twice the steel-wheel cost, but Maglev elevated guideways and superior climbing ability makes it a more logical choice for hilly terrain's and maglev's quick starts and stops.

A Swedish train can run on existing railroad tracks using a special lifting mechanism to negotiate curves at high speeds. It will be tested and put into service along Amtrak's Northeast Corridor and it would be good for national and international travelers destined for the 2012 Summer Olympic Games.

Companies in Pennsylvania, New York, and Vermont wants to be licensed to build maglev trains in the United States. In figure 8.10 is a TGV in final assembly. European rail suppliers have big backlogs and some foreign company builders welcome North American's partnerships because of the money and the potential.

Fig. 8.10. French TGV assembly plant.

New Work in The US

The United States will be taking needed steps for fast comfortable rides on steel-wheel or maglev trains. Our railroad transportation systems are so obsolete and have lasted so long, new design changes will contribute tremendously. When we read about freight and passenger trains being derailed in different parts of the country, they are caused by old signaling devices or aged rails. The complete transportation systems needs to be updated with new design changes.

Many travelers would be very interested in a train system that travels at distances up to 300 miles. Most of our obsolete transportation systems have been operating approximately 70 years with not many changes being made. On the other side of the spectrum, our population has tremendously grown and more cars and airplanes are being manufactured with large amounts of money spent yearly.

Orders for new airplanes would go to Boeing that subcontracts components to foreign companies overseas. It subcontracts more work in France than the Airbus competitor. McDonnell Douglas is another company that has subcontractors in the Peoples Republic of China and other countries abroad. When more highways are built, more cars will come from Japan, Italy, Germany, France and other countries. We need to provide more work for the Americans especially in the year of 2002 and into the future.

Maryland based Lockheed Martin Corporation that won a $200 billion Joint Strike Fighter contract on October 26, 2001 received more than 260,000 resumes in 2002 and they are still being submitted. The bad part is, Lockheed has 2,500 positions to fill for the entire project over the next few years. The jobs calls for high-level aeronautical engineers and you only get that experience working on a Fights program said Stout. They have only hired a handful of workers.

If we look at the yearly increases in population, number of vehicles and airplanes being manufactured, pollution growth, vehicle traffic growth, vehicle accidents, death, funds spent for all forms of transportation, loss of productive hours, loss in personal time, and lost in fuel because of congestion, we will know it requires a new transporation system.

I have provided detail information of a wide cross section of events that we have now and what the events may create in the future. The purpose is to help stimulate positive action from information received. In the past there was surveying, right-of-ways located and made, hard labor, and trains. The train opened a new life for

Americans and caused an economic surge. That advantage was the tremendous driving force for our economic growth.

Contributions To The Future

Many people are not aware of our world conditions pertaining to our health, daily cost, lost of lives, and conditions that are sure to continue in this world. We may not be aware of some things that are taking place overseas and in America, but must realize this is all one planet. What happens in one part affects all of our lives. The cross-section of relevant events is based on airplanes, vehicles, and our other fuel burning vehicles as contributors in an effort to show the need for more use of trains for our transportation. More trains will be available in the near future.

Continuum is something absolutely continuous and homogeneous of which no distinction of content can be affirmed except by reference to something else. We cannot stop time to catch up, we have to reflect on the past and plan and react positively for the future. New trains are being built updating the complete transportation system and more people are riding the trains after the terrorist attack and the airline cutbacks. This should be a growing event as more people leave the present mode of transportation and discover a new way of traveling in comfort on trains.

We can all participate in ways in the present and in the future that will slow some of the events that are changing our lives. We know some answers to the equations, but we have to use a number of ways to try and reach the answers we want and need.

Select Bibliography

Books

Johnson, James C. "Contemporary Transportation." *Prentice Hall Inc.* U.S. Army War College, 1996.

Lynch, Thomas. "High Speed Rail in the US Super Trains for the Millenium." *Cordon and Breach Science Publishers,* (1998).

Moon, Francis C. "Superconducting Levitation." *Jonh Wiley & Sons Inc.* (1994).

Sussman, Joseph. "Introduction to Transportation Systems." *Artch House, Inc.* Norwood, MA.

Vranich, Joseph, "Super-Trains. Solutions to American's Transportation Gridlock." *St Margin's Press:* New York, NY (1991).

Documents

-------,"Final Report On The National Maglev Initiative." *National Transportation Library.* (Nov 18, 2000): p1-90.

Schrank, Davie. Lomac, Davie. "Urban Roadway Congestion." *Texas Transportation Institute Annual Report, Texas A&M University.* (1998).

Sicilian, Eric. "Monorail: Back to the Future." *Mit's Technology Review*, March/April 1998.

Magazines

Omalley, Christopher. "Rapid Rails." *Popular Science*, (1992).

Scott, Gourley R. "Track to The Future." Magnetic Levitation Trains. *Popular Mechanics.* (May 1998). v175 n5 p 68(4).

-------, "The Train Is Leaving The Depot." *US News & World Report,* (March 2001).

Schrank, Davie. Lomax, Tim. "Urban Roadway Congestion." *Texas Transportation Institute Annual Report*, *Texas A&M University,* (1998, 2002, 2003).

Shute, Nancy. "The Weather Turns Wild." *US News & World Report*, March 19, 2001.

-------, "Expansion Seen For Air Cargo Industry." *Aviation Week & Technology,* (January 2001).

-------, "Magnetic Levitation, Maglev." *The Supertrain In Maryland.* M/Q, (Nov 18, 2001).

-------, "Swords to Plowshares-or Trains." *Discover.,* (Nov 1995) j16 n11.

Articles

Bahn, Deutsche. "Germany Intercity Express-High Speed Rail Network, Germany." *In Projects Business & Finance.* (Dec 7, 2001).

-------, Maglev Trains: A Permanent Solution? *The Economist (US).* (Oct 31, 1998) p88 (1).

-------, "Track To The Future."

-------, "A Better Way To Fly." *Railway Innovations.* (Feb 21, 1998) v346 n8056 p213.

O'Connor, Leo. "MAGNETIC Levitation Vehicles: *Mechanical Engineering*. (Aug 1993) v115 issue 8 p74 4p, 1c.

Ritter, Johannes. "Transrapid's Subsidized Future at Home Looks Bright When Seen From China." *Business & Finance.* (Dec 7, 2001).

-------, "Germany Intercity Express-High Speed Rail Network." *Industry Projects.* (Dec 2001).

-------, "TGV France-High Speed Rail Network, France." *Industry Projects.* (Dec 2001).

Silber, Kenneth. "Magnetic Trains Ride Fast Track to Nowhere." *In Sight On The News.* (August 29, 1994): v10 n35 p 4(3).

Siuru, Bill. "Swiss to Bury Their Mag-Lev." *Mass Transit.* (May-June 1997). v23 n3 p46(2).

Siuru, Bill. "Everbody-but Everybody-Is Joining The High Speed Rail Club." *Mass Transit.* (Sept-Oct 1997): v23 n5 p44(5).

Wilkins, Van. "High Speed Rail Is On The Way." *Mass Transit.* (June 2000): v26 i4 p54.

-------, "SERAPHIM: Adapting Mag-Lev for Existing Trackage." *Mass Transit.* (Nov-Dec 1995).

Newspapers

Brelis, Matthew. "For Airlines, Forecast Is Still A Stormy One." *The Boston Globe*, (2001).

-------. "Clinton Takes Aim At Air Traffic Delays." *The Boston Globe*, (2001).

"Cleaned for Sleep off." *The Boston Globe,* (Jan 18, 2001).

Chandler, David. "A Berg's Eye View of Antarctica." *The Boston Globe.* (Sept 14, 2000).

Flanigan, James. "Maglev and L.A.'s Needs May Be On Opposite Poles." *The Los Angles Times*, (Oct 1999).

Helzer, Bill. "Decision Nears On City To Get Maglev Prototype." *Pittsburgh Post.* (Sept 2000).

Jasdanun, Amic. "High-tech Train Travel." *Associated Press.* (Nov 18, 2000).

Morago, Greg. "Wide Seats, Great Food, Taking The A Train." *The Boston Globe*, (2001).

Reuters. "Study of Air Separation Rule Queried." *The Boston Globe.* (Feb 9, 2001).

About the Author

He worked as a Senior Design Engineer in aircraft-manufacturing and Senior Engineer on the Service Module of the Apollo Spacecraft. He also built two commercial buildings and managed a successful business for sixteen years from his office in engineering. He has written to college Professors, US Representatives, US Senators, Governors, Transportation Managers, Transportation Planners, and Town Managers concerning Traffic Congestion and how it can be overcome with Commuter-Rail, and High Speed Rail.

Printed in the United Kingdom
by Lightning Source UK Ltd.
101492UKS00002B/199